Derby Porcelain 1750-1798

The Stag Lodge.

This was the old crest of Derby

and was known locally as 'The Buck in the Park'.

William Duesbury 1725–1786

William Duesbury II 1763–1797

Elizabeth Edwards, daughter of a Derby solicitor. Married to William Duesbury II January 4th, 1787. Later married to Michael Kean.

It is thought that both miniature portraits may have been painted by Michael Kean.

Derby Porcelain 1750-1798

Gilbert Bradley
with
Judith Anderson
and
Robin Barkla

Foreword by
JVG Mallet

British Library Cataloguing in Publication Data
Bradley, Gilbert 1917-
    Derby Porcelain 1750-1798.
    1. Derby Porcelain, history
    I. Title
    738.27

First published in 1990 by
Thomas Heneage & Co. Ltd.
1 Stewart's Court,
220 Stewart's Road,
London SW8 4UD.

ISBN 0-946708-25-8

Designed by Aplin King Associates.

Contents

Foreword by JVG Mallet   6

Introduction   9

The Duesbury Papers by Judith Anderson   12

The Early Years   26

Animals and Birds   31

Early Wares of the 'Dry-Edge' Period   40

Figures in the 'Dry-Edge' Period   42

Experimental and 'Transitional' Pieces   46

Useful and Decorative Wares of the
'Patch Mark' Period   49

Figures in the Early 'Patch Mark' Period   65

Later 'Patch Mark' Figures   74

Unglazed Porcelain Figures   85

Ornamental Vases   95

Domestic Ware for the Tea Table   112

Botanical Decoration on Porcelain   147

Blue and White   170

Foreword

JVG Mallet

The reputation of eighteenth century Derby porcelain has suffered from unsuitable comparisons. One of the factory's early proprietors, William Duesbury I, bears some blame for this because he had the cheek to market his ware as 'the Second Dresden'. Worse still for Derby's renown has been the comparison with Chelsea porcelain. During the nineteenth century collectors fell into the error of attributing much pre-1770 Derby figure-production to Chelsea, with the result that when Bernard Rackham and others cleared up this confusion in the 1920s, many disgruntled owners were left with the impression that their porcelain figures, which were of course no worse than before, had in some sense been demoted.

It is in no small degree due to the activities of the Derby International Porcelain Society that in the last few years we have begun to admire eighteenth century Derby porcelain for its own virtues rather than seeing it as a pale reflection of Dresden (ie Meissen) or of Chelsea. One step in this process of re-evaluation was the holding at Derby Museum and Art Gallery of the exhibition commemorated in this book. Essentially the exhibition was drawn from the riches of Derby Museum's own holdings, though supplemented here and there by pieces from private collections. Since no illustrated catalogue of the Museum's remarkable collection has ever been published, this in itself will be a big step forward.

The pieces illustrated and described represent Derby porcelain from the period covered by the proprietorship of the elder and younger William Duesbury, but reaching backwards in time to cover also what we believe to be the factory's beginnings under Andrew Planché in the early 1750s. The story of the factory and the sequence of its productions will be found described, in the pages that follow, by Gilbert Bradley and his fellow authors, so I will not attempt to anticipate what will be better said by them. Rather, I find myself asking which, if any, of Derby's productions earn it the right to consideration as one of the great European porcelain factories of the eighteenth century?

To the Derby enthusiast no product of the factory is wholly without interest, but four categories of Derby porcelain spring most particularly to my mind for high aesthetic quality: the early 'dry edge' figures; certain wares of the late fifties and early sixties very decoratively painted with birds, cherries and moths; some of the biscuit porcelain figures of the Chelsea-Derby period and of the years immediately succeeding it; the best of the landscape and botanical painting of the eighteenth century's closing decades.

I realise that champions may leap forward to defend the doll-like 'pale face' figures of the late 1750s, the blue and white of all periods, the Neo-classical vases and wares of the Chelsea-Derby period or the flowers of William Billingsley. I grant that each of these categories includes pieces with particular attractions, but Derby's figure-modelling in between the Planché period and 1770, when Derby absorbed the Chelsea factory, seems to me to lack the originality and ambition that are prerequisites for consideration in the highest categories of ceramic or any other art. The blue and white of Derby, for its part, seldom rises above the general level of serviceable design that we take for granted from Worcester and Bow. In Neo-classical porcelain Derby had the field for many years almost to itself, yet allowed itself to be anticipated and frequently outshone by Wedgwood's stonewares despite the head-start their more prestigious material should have conferred on the Derby managers. As for Billingsley, even if we forgive him his fussy little pink roses, he was during his time at Derby a figure quite secondary in importance by comparison with Zachariah Boreman, Wright of Derby's friend, and the man who above all others adapted the English watercolour tradition to the technique and decorative needs of china-painting.

No, Derby's claims to a place among the great European porcelain factories of the eighteenth century may rest on my four categories. Think of the 'dry edge' Chinoiserie groups symbolising the Senses; the finest work attributed to the so-called 'Moth-Painter'; the biscuit figures ordered by Vulliamy as ornaments for his gilt-metal clock-cases; the best of the wares painted with landscape or botanical subjects if not by, then under the eye of Zachariah Boreman. Such things need fear no comparisons with the best of their kind in Europe.

Introduction

The two William Duesburys, father and son, owned and managed the Derby China Works on Nottingham Road for much of the second half of the eighteenth century. William Duesbury the elder (1725-86) was the son of a Cannock carrier and owned a decorating establishment in London before moving to Derby. The unsigned Agreement dated January 1756, between John Heath, the banker (who is described as 'Gentleman'), Andrew Planché ('China Maker') and William Duesbury (of Longton 'in ye county of Stafford, Enamellor'), stipulates that they were bound together 'in ye Art of making English China as also in buying and selling all sorts of Wares belonging to ye Art of making China'.[1]

Duesbury lost no time in making his presence felt and after the 19 April, 1756, he was responsible for a considerable enlargement of the factory. The success of his achievement is proved by the fact that he was able in 1770, with the financial assistance of John Heath, to purchase the prestigious but failing Chelsea Porcelain Factory. One has only to view the early Derby wares of the 1756-70 period and compare them with the Chelsea-Derby period to see the great strides that Duesbury I had made in porcelain production, creating a strong body which was capable of consistent, and sophisticated modelling. The handling of the items, changes which followed the introduction of soapstone in the 1760s, or the acquisition of the bone-ash recipes of Chelsea, are equally a testament to the elder Duesbury's abilities. The moulds that were acquired increased his range and the enamel colours were improved.

Duesbury took over the Castle Tavern in Bedford Street, Covent Garden, to create a London showroom for his wares and in a letter sent from London to Mrs Duesbury, dated 25 June, 1773, he states 'we sign and seal tomorrow'. William Wood was appointed the first London manager. Although it appears that William Duesbury was granted the Royal Appointment in 1775, the first mention of a royal visit, is a 'press release' sent by Wood to Duesbury for his approval, dated 25 June, 1776, announcing the forthcoming visit of the Queen accompanied by the Duchess of Ancaster. This took place on 23 July and Wood was able to report:

> On Friday last her Majesty accompanied with the Duchess of Ancaster was pleased to honour with her presence Mr Duesbury's Ware Rooms in Bedford Street, Covent Garden. Condescended to express great approbation at these Beautiful articles of Derby and Chelsea Porcelain and Paintings and Encouraged the same by making some purchases.[2]

Wood's messages were brief and to the point and the general impression of his role at this time is largely one of debt collector and payer of bills in London 'for there was a great dearth of money on the books'. In 1777, Joseph Lygo was appointed as Wood's successor, but there is little surviving correspondence between Lygo and Duesbury I and it is not until the following decade, shortly before William Duesbury's death, in 1786, when Lygo's letters begin to his son, William Duesbury II, that one is able to gather more information. Between July 1786 and December 1795, there are well over five hundred letters that have been preserved.

In order to keep abreast of fashion the Derby factory, which had first copied Meissen, imitated or made direct copies of Sèvres shapes — the inspirations obvious in many Billingsley examples. Patterns were also copied and Mr Catherine, the modeller, was asked by Lygo to make sketch drawings of Sèvres figures which were being sold by Mr Christie. Lygo also purchased odd and even broken pieces of china which he kept at the showroom and used for comparisons. French shapes and patterns dominated the market and even the declaration of war against France in February 1793, seemed to have little effect on fashion. A Derby set, decorated with insects was 'very ill done to what the French ones are' (22 May, 1794); and on 18 February, 1795, Lygo wrote that French tureens were 'the best shapes about'.

On June 7, 1789, Lygo reported on Mr Christie's three-day sale of Sèvres, and how goods sold very cheaply, hoping this would 'sicken them from importing to this country'. And another sale of quality French china 'sold astonishingly low indeed. I should think for nearly half the price it cost in the country ... at great deficiency by and by' (22 July, 1789) and yet the sales continued even though this was after the Fall of the Bastille.

Despite the Revolution, French porcelain still flooded the English market, 'for the people in general seems to be mad after it' (25 November, 1790); 'the great importation of French china is amazing' wrote the showroom manager (10 March, 1791), and previous good sellers like *déjeuners*, were no longer wanted for 'the town is quite full of French ones' (13 January, 1791). Even previously reliable customers, like the Irish dealers, were reported to have got into the habit of going over to France to buy inexpensive china. Duesbury obviously considered selling French wares in the London showroom, but Lygo suggested 'it will hurt our sale of goods with the trade' (2 December, 1790).

The services of French workmen, presumably refugees, remained cheap and the warehouse was able to employ enamellers at only 30 to 35 shillings a week, but Lygo regarded them 'as indifferent hands'.[3] However, in spite of the war, there was no patriotic feeling to support home-produced wares and even Mrs Fitzherbert appears to have rejected a number of special plates in favour of a French product.

It would seem that Derby lost orders due to their high prices, when compared to the French; and also because of their trade delivery. A special armorial service for Sir Frank Ford seems to have been placed with the cheaper French shop, after Derby had produced a fine sample plate, 'but it was too long in hand' in March, 1794.

Both Duesbury's used a mixture of Derby apprentice-trained and skilled outside workmen and until about 1795, the management at Derby appear to have had no real difficulty in attracting and keeping their work force. Local boys were taken on for seven years to learn the various skills of painting, repairing, and preparing colour.

Although William Duesbury I did not die until October 30, 1786, his son effectively became joint manager of the China Works in 1784, and immediately wished to make some changes within the factory. Possibly the son may have been prone to rush into things without the natural caution of his father and for this reason an agreement between the two men was drawn up (3 February, 1785) which restricted the building, for the next two years, of any offices other than 'the store or drying room, the dayroom or cellar and the cool room with stair case'.

Unfortunately there is little information concerning the actual day to day running of the factory. It would appear that Duesbury II appointed a manager to deputise for him during his absences from the works, such as visiting the London warehouse; and from about 1784 into the early 1790s, the gilder Joseph Stables assumed this role. During these periods he would write to his employer of events, including sales and other problems.

Stables appears to have been a good communicator at all levels, efficiently passing on information for goods required. Like Lygo, Stables was obviously proud of the factory's abilities, and would boast enthusiastically: 'Lord Cremone's Mug is beatiful . . . Can the great town find one more so?' (30 April, 1789).

Following Stables departure, probably in the summer of 1793, Charles King assumed responsibility during Duesbury's periods of absence: reporting, two years later that 'everything goes on peacefully but not with that propriety and dispatch which a good overlooker might be the means of', and Duesbury, who was then on holiday in the Lake District, was informed of 'the necessity of your presence in this critical situation of affairs' and required to return.

In December 1795, Michael Kean was taken into partnership heralding the close of the Duesbury era.

The Duesbury Papers

Judith Anderson

The 'Duesbury Papers' is the collective name given to a huge quantity of surviving documents, mainly of eighteenth century date, that relate to the Duesbury family and its business, and are presently housed at the Local Studies Library (administered by Derbyshire County Council), Derby. Unfortunately there are no records to indicate the exact provenance of the papers, but it is presumed that the manuscripts were presented to the then combined town library and museum in October, 1914, as part of the Bemrose Collection of local history books and documents. William Bemrose is well established as a late Victorian author, researcher and collector of Derby Porcelain and related material. However his unique collection was split-up at his death in 1909; many of his ceramics were sold at auction in Nottingham that year, and he bequeathed to the British Museum a number of important Duesbury and early Derby factory documents, including Duesbury's *London Account Book* (1751-1755).

Within Jewitt's account of the Derby factory in the *Ceramic Art of Great Britain,* printed in 1878, are quotes from documents now in the Local Studies Library, Derby. Most notable are letters from the London showroom manager, Lygo, to Duesbury II. A piece of research addressed to Jewitt at Winster Hall and stamped 1868, which refers to the Billingsley and Walker families, has survived within the bulk of the 'Duesbury Papers' though not by any means all of Jewitt's documentation is in Derby. Some Duesbury papers were at one time lodged with, or given, by Jewitt, to the Victoria and Albert Museum, which include work-lists of John Brewer and Askew, some letters and indentures. Other Bemrose-owned pieces seem to have disappeared altogether, obvious examples being the original 'Plan of Mr Duesbury's Garden, House and Manufactory' relating to the 1815 lease as published in *Bow, Chelsea and Derby,* and the famous silhouette portrait of the elder Duesbury.

Derby City Museum and Art Gallery also own a few documentary records from the eighteenth century China Works, that may have been part of the original 1914 parcel from the Bemrose Library. The City Museum's pieces however consist largely of the more visually interesting examples: small rough sketches with costings for a new pattern; designs for Chelsea-Derby vases and late 1790s plans and proposed alterations to the factory.

It is believed that at least some of the Bemrose papers relating to the Duesburys were given to him by Mr Huish, a Derby solicitor, in 1889. Perhaps some documents could have been available or common to both Jewitt and Bemrose?

Most of the information and observations in this chapter derive from those 'Duesbury Papers' in the Local Studies Library, Derby. First impressions of this collection include its huge size, and difficulty in finding specific documents. Some papers are only two-inch scraps while others are folded letters; there are legal agreements on vellum and small notebooks. The manuscripts' actual contents are equally diverse, as one might expect of the contents of the Duesbury's own desk/bureau: with important documents filed for safety, but also chatty family letters, notes or doodles that are surprisingly preserved, perhaps quickly slipped into a drawer in an attempt to tidy the working surface. Most of these extraneous papers appear to date to the later 1780s and 1790s and Duesbury II's management, which may indicate something of the character of the young factory owner. Included is a bundle of the Duesbury's household bills that hint at the quality of life of a middle-class Derbeian family with accounts for example, from grocers, seed and cheese suppliers as well as the haberdashers, and, significantly, the payment for French lessons for the young William Duesbury. They also indicate that it was common business practice to allow two or more years of credit to accumulate before payment for goods was expected: an important factor in the attempt to administer successfully the China Works' finances. Other piles of documents which do not directly relate to the Derby factory include Kean's personal accounts and Richard Egan's correspondence from Bath. Egan was a china dealer and was married to Anne, William Duesbury's eldest daughter.

Many of the business papers survive without reference to their original context and yet they can provide intriguing snippets of information. For example within a group of IOUs and receipts for money belonging to Duesbury II and the flower painter William Billingsley in the 1790s, is an odd one dated 1766 that obviously represents a contract between their respective fathers. Perhaps the ex-Chelsea decorator, Billingsley senior, did out-work for the China Works before his death in 1770, and the elder Duesbury felt it incumbent upon him to employ the sixteen-year-old Billingsley, aware of his likely talents and background, at an atypical apprentice rate of 5 shillings per week for five years.

1756 to 1784

Unfortunately, the documents dating to the period 1756-1784, and before the closure of the Chelsea factory, are severely limited, and information to be gleaned from them even more restricted. The papers do include two pocket notebooks listing the large quantities and quality of wood acquired from Derbyshire woods used for firing.

There are nine apprenticeship indentures, and articles of agreement covering twelve other employees; both groups relate to all aspects of the manufactory. They include the following apprentices: George Bradbury (repairer, 10 March, 1765), John Winrow (painter, 6 June, 1765), John Frost (painter, to serve a remainder of his term, 16 April, 1770), Thomas Southall (painter, 25 December, 1772), William Smith (to prepare colours and paint under his father, Constantine, 28 October, 1773), William Cooper (painter, 1 January, 1777), John Porter (painter, 7 April, 1777), John Morlidge (repairer, 21 August, 1777), and William Smith (son of Hannah, to prepare colours 23 November, 1778). In 1772 firemen for 'glazing and burning' agreed to accept 6 shillings a week for three years: they included David Keene, Joseph Heald, Jacob Spooner, Robert Woodward, Thomas Wardle, Samuel Weaver, William Whitehall, J. Butler and William Yates. Contracts still exist between Duesbury and William Gadsby (mould maker, agreement for four years at 10s a week, 2 September, 1772), Edward Phillips (painter, agreement for £1 5s a week, 2 September, 1772) and William Hand (undated, to serve one year at either factory as 'handle and . . . of china').

Another list notes when eight workers arrived in two sections, 1774-1776, in the repairing and throwing rooms of the factory: William Moore (11 April, 1774), Edward Belfield (19 September, 1775), John Morlidge (26 September, 1775, which conflicts with the apprenticeship date above), Thomas Trundle (22 April, 1776), Joseph Shipley (16 September, 1776), and as painters Robert Penington (6 November, 1775), Thomas Broughton (19 August, 1776), and Cooper (16 April, 1776).

The only well known artists named in this period are Gauron, a 'very ingenious modeller from Tournay' (who wanted to come to England according to a letter to Duesbury from the dealer Thomas Morgan, probably in 1770), and 'Mr. Stephan' whose bills for the purchase in London of '13 French prints from Sayer and Bennet' and 'a print of Andromache and another of Cleopatra' (used as sources for decoration), from Messrs. Ryland and Coustos were receipted in September 1774. There are a number of intriguing financial negotiations between Duesbury I and well-known porcelain families. For example, William Billingsley senior gave the factory proprietor an IOU for £10 in 1766, William and Alice Pardoe received five guineas on 10 June, 1779, and J. Brewer was paid £2-9s-3d on 31 December, 1782.

A very simple pocket account book belonging to Duesbury I is dated November 1773-74. It contains little more than lists of names and payments, without reference to services rendered, but the following entries are of interest: 'paid of Mr Jam Giles his draft a 6 weeks £71- 11s.' (7 February, 1774), and, almost indecipherable, 'for employing the Deares' (possibly some connection with the modeller John Deare, who wrote to his employer, Duesbury, on 30 August, 1784), while Mr Cunningham was paid five guineas for a model of 'Macaley' (Miss Macaulay, the historian) in December 1773.

A letter to Mrs Duesbury from her husband in London is dated 25 June, 1773 and records the acquisition of the china warehouse in the capital, 'it was the Castle Tavern in Bedford Street, Covent Garden . . . we sign and seal tomorrow.' William Wood was Duesbury's London agent and manager of the company's Covent Garden showroom from its opening in 1773. Wood communicated with the Derby factory by letter but there are few surviving examples, and most of these are in appallingly shattered condition. Wood's messages were brief and to the point. The general impression of Wood's role in 1776 is largely one of debt collector and payer of bills in London 'for there was a great dearth of money on the books'. A few more specific details can be found such as Wood's request for the factory to make 'button flatts' for he had met someone who could take 'all we can make' (15 October, 1776); and one of the factory's leading exporters, Mr Williams, purchased £1,900 of goods the following week for shipment abroad. On 25 June, 1776, Wood sent Duesbury a 'press release' for his approval to announce the visit to the factory of the Queen with the Duchess of Ancaster. There is no record of any earlier royal visit within the 'Duesbury Papers'. Legal papers relating to Duesbury's ownership of the Sucstone Mine and Brassington Liberty are dated 1776 and 1778. But these documents do not record why the mine was acquired; ownership of other property, locally or in London, seems to have been an investment rather than a resource, along with stocks and shares.

Other documents of the early 1780s period are of minor business interest, recording, for example, the odd bill for transporting lime from Breedon and Crich, or coals from the Derby Wharf. Various small bills of 1782, combined with a factory account book compiled the following year sighting payments to members of the Duesbury family, surprisingly indicate they were the responsibility of Duesbury I's daughter Anne, then aged about nineteen, and before she married Egan.

Joseph Lygo was appointed as Wood's successor in 1777, but there is also little surviving correspondence between Lygo and Duesbury I.

The Lygo Letters 1786 to 1796

From July 1786 until December 1795 there are well over five hundred letters from Lygo in London to the Derby China Works, amounting to the largest single group of documents in the 'Duesbury Papers'. It would be interesting to know why this sudden profusion of letters exists and it may represent a deliberate change of policy in the nature of how the business was run under Duesbury II. For example, the two venues could have become administratively more independent; Duesbury II certainly did not visit London very often and Lygo may have acquired more day to day authority; thus written communication became more vital. Sadly, information about the earlier management is so sparse that one cannot directly compare details about marketing or technical processes, although it is likely that the son inherited and continued many of the elder Duesbury's practices.

Unfortunately this most informative correspondence is almost without exception one way. Nevertheless the Lygo letters give a fascinating insight into the Duesbury family and its business. Also included is a comparison of other factories' goods, notably Worcester, and the ceramic trade and trends in general. At first Lygo wrote to the younger Duesbury on average two or three times a week, and sometimes daily, although letters become shorter and less frequent with time. For the year 1789 there are 84 surviving Lygo letters, for 1795 only 46. Long gaps in the correspondence seem to indicate

Duesbury's occasional visits to London (lasting generally a couple of weeks), or sometimes illness.

The quantity and range of information in the Lygo letters is considerable, whereas Wood's letters were brief half-foolscap size, Lygo's are often two to four full pages long. Alongside the business reports is news from family friends and relatives (notably the wayward brother, James), details of the stock market, political comments and an update on the affairs of royalty, especially the Prince of Wales's financial situation or George III's health. Lygo was also instructed to purchase barrels of fish, wines, clothing and carpets for the family in Derby, and letters tell of his success in tracking down personal goods.

That such a close relationship should develop between Lygo and Duesbury II may come as a surprise, but there was possibly a social connection between the two families, for Lygo's parents lived in Church Broughton, a small village about twelve miles to the west of Derby, this being the parish of the Rev. Chawner, Duesbury II's brother-in-law. The letters nevertheless are always formally addressed and signed 'Sir, your very obedient servant'.

It is impossible to give all the business details included in the nine and a half years of Lygo's letters, and many examples are already well reported in the various Derby porcelain reference books. However some are worth quoting in full and in their original context, such as Lygo's suggestion to finish badly fired white ware not 'anything like our patterns but rather like Worcester' (2 July, 1786), and the various details of the Duke of Clarence's 'Hope' 'crockery' in 1791.

Factory management

Until about 1795 the management at Derby appeared to have no real difficulty in attracting and keeping their work force. Both Duesburys used a mixture of Derby apprentice-trained and skilled outside workmen. A number of early legal agreements and apprenticeship indentures survive to show the sound apprenticeship scheme in place for local boys for seven years to learn the various skills of painting, repairing, and preparing colours. It is well recorded how failure to honour the terms, such as absenting oneself from work without permission, could result in imprisonment; both Brocklesbury and Spängler were arrested in December 1792. Employees generally seemed to believe the Duesburys were fair, with history portraying Kean as a villain, given to hot-headed bouts of temper. But it will be seen that the factory was already in turmoil well before Kean became Duesbury's partner and Kean may well have been taken on as a 'trouble-shooter'.

Factory efficiency under Duesbury II

Within a few months of the younger Duesbury effectively becoming joint manager of the China Works in 1784 it is obvious that he wished to make immediate changes within the factory. Some 'intended alterations' seem to have been the father's ideas, as indicated by a scrap of paper annotated and dated 26 September, 1784 which appears to be written in the elder man's hand (Derby City Museum). However, Duesbury II may well have rushed into things without his father's caution resulting in the agreement between the two Duesburys (3 February, 1785) for improving the drying and cool rooms. That winter he complained to the Canal Committee that their failure to finish the canal banks had 'caused great inconvenience' for he had 'not been able to lay out rooms in the manufactory to best advantage fearing floods' (12 December, 1785). Factory security was also tightened-up by the imposition of five shilling fines on anyone found in a part of the works where they had no business to be (23 November, 1787), with a final reminder on 24 September, 1788. There had obviously been some back door pilfering within the works, for Stables wrote to Duesbury about a china set no.55 he had seen being sold at Alfreton market for seven guineas, and notes previous sightings there of white ware three years earlier (5 May, 1790).

Duesbury II also sought to make the factory more efficient, for example by instigating a clocking-in procedure and a number of time and motion studies. Lygo records the details of a wooden clock, devised with a piece of paper to the hour-hand, that would give employees three minutes to sign in (3 September, 1788). Included in such work in 1792 was the repairer Thomas Mason, who had been apprenticed to Duesbury on the 2 September, 1772, at one guinea per week, and who agreed 'to use a stop watch to make observations of work done... with the utmost truth and accuracy' yet without detection by fellow employees. A record survives of Mason's observation of what he 'commonly thinks proper to do of a day' relating to the throwing, pressing and turning of wares, including plates, basins, saucers, tea cups, ice pails, tea pots and sugar boxes. There are calculations for costing out the time taken by the gilders to do set patterns (such as pattern 208, which cost twopence for gilding, 10 July, 1792), and also an undated letter of complaint signed by ten gilders (Sims, Rogers, Webster, Longden, Clark, Samuel Keys, William Cooper, John Yates, Stables and Barton) objecting to Duesbury's proposals to reduce the payment for certain patterns without consultation — they also added that their wages were late. In November 1794 Martin Stevens, William Horsley and Thomas Rogers also agreed to become secret timekeepers. Stevens' contract included the working of extra hours, keeping a book to record each worker's times, with a financial forfeit if found to be falsifying times to anyone's advantage to the value of ten times such credit.

The period around 1790-95 also sees the revision of employment contracts. A draft agreement between Duesbury and 'such painters of this manufactory whose names are here subscribed' dates to 1793 and contains changes in conditions of employment, including pay of 3s 6d a day, a working week of six 10½-hour days, piece work when appropriate, forbidding of outside decorating, a six-month period of notice and an agreement not to enter anyone else's employ as a painter unless one's services had been offered back to Derby first. Barrett and Thorpe (*op. cit.* pp.129-30) quote a similar undated document signed by known gilders, and also one whereby Boreman received very preferential treatment including a secret rate twice the value with more open hours. However Banford complained in February 1794 of his 'optic nerves... strained for eighteen shillings a week less than Boreman and ten hours a day'. It is possible that Duesbury tried to impose work by the piece on some of his best decorators *c.*1795, as typified by an undated contract drawn up for Brewer (until his debts were cleared), with figures and landscapes paid by an elaborate formula measured by the fraction of the inch, combined with varying backgrounds. Flowers were paid by quality and number rather than size.

Duesbury's attempts to get more out of his talented artists only resulted in unrest. Boreman appears to have left Derby sometime in late 1794, and by 30 January, 1795 did 'not now have the least thought of returning with the idea of doing landscapes at 1/6 each... for it was out of the power of any man in the manufactory to copy two of his coloured landscapes a day'. This seems to indicate payment by the piece. Complin too felt badly treated by Duesbury as 'my hair admits of more respect' (18 September, 1794). Lygo's letter to Duesbury after he had heard of Billingsley's intended departure (1 August, 1795, to help John Coke at Pinxton) particularly highlights the consequences of low staff morale 'for it will be a great loss to loose such a hand and not only that but his going into another factory will put them in the way of doing flowers in the same way which they are at present intirely ignorant in.' The outstanding artists — Boreman, Banford, Billingsley and Complin — all left Duesbury's employment within eighteen months of each other.

A rough draft contract survives dated 1790 offering William Smith, the colour maker and painter, the opportunity to decorate at the lowest piece rate, but more importantly to work for four shillings a week more to experiment on recipes and preparation of colours. The document tells of a £500 fine for disclosing any secrets, and a £100 penalty for entering into anyone else's employment without offering his services back to Derby first. The workforce's motivation was indeed at a very low ebb during the summer of 1795, when Charles King was left in charge of the works, with the business in 'such a state' (as he says in a letter to Duesbury in August 1795), while his employer was on holiday in the Lake District, that even the likes of Mr Smith wanted to quit after more than twenty years at Derby because he did not like the smell of turpentine.

Some of the London-based artists seemed to have been in a position to negotiate better terms of work, like Richard Askew's 5s 3d a day (2 August, 1794, though most references quote this document wrongly as by the piece). The very troublesome Spängler tried to get his salary increased in December 1794 (24 December), from his £150 a year, plus £50 equipment, though Lygo believed Duesbury would 'never be able to manage him on any other plan' than payment of two shillings per inch for each figure modelled. New 'replacement' hands were perhaps treated with more respect for John Brewer wanted and was guaranteed one pound eleven shillings a week (11 April, 1795), and 'Jockey' Hill received two and a half guineas for a fifty-four hour week to paint landscapes.

The Derby management frequently lent small sums of money to their employees, for example five guineas was frequently given to new workers by Lygo to help fund their transport up to Derby. Whether this was a paternalistic action on the part of their new employers or a shrewd move to ensure workers' future cooperation, we can but guess. The result was instant debt and obligation for many men, including the likes of Banford (who received two guineas on 25 August, 1789), Withers (who requested seven guineas on 17 September, 1789), Spängler (who had his £1-11s-6d coach fare paid and a further borrowed five guineas, lent on 14 July, 1790), and John Brewer (who borrowed five guineas on 25 May, 1795). Their debts were removed from their weekly wages till cleared, with Withers being docked 4s from his 21s pay. The apprentice Brocklesbury, after absconding in December 1792, refused to lose a quarter of his income in this manner and opted to walk the hundred and thirty miles back to Derby instead. By the mid 1790s some decorators had large debts, with Banford complaining it was impossible for five people to live on eleven shillings a week (13 March, 1795).

Unfortunately there is little information concerning the actual day to day running of the factory. It would appear that Duesbury appointed a manager who deputised in his absence, such as when visiting the London warehouse. From about 1784 into the early 1790s the gilder Joseph Stables assumed this role. During Stables' management he would write to his employer about events, sales or problems at Derby. Stables must have been a capable replacement for on 19 September, 1788, he was forewarned that the Duchess of Devonshire was to call, with two gentlemen, and was initially 'at a loss and fear I can not give her every information she will expect' — which would seem to indicate that there were no Pattern Books available to show her — but then remembered there were the Duke of Bedford's cups she could inspect. Stables appears to have been a good communicator at all levels, efficiently passing on information for goods required, and aware of his colleagues' feelings, such as Mason's dislike of Spängler for 'Mason never can speak with patience of him' (24 January, 1789). Stables, like Lygo, was obviously proud of the factory's abilities and boasted enthusiastically: 'Lord Cremone's mug is beautiful... can the great town find one more so? (30 April, 1789). For some reason the middle-aged Stables seems to have left the factory about 1793, and went off to war. An undated letter to Duesbury reports that the winter campaign has not deterred the officers and men, and that they were likely to march to Scotland, but; 'two of our men to swing at Bedford on Saturday, and one to Botany.'

Mr Charles King appears to have assumed the responsibility of manager by the summer of 1793.

SEEKING RAW MATERIALS

One of the most frequently posed questions relating to the old Derby China Works concerns the source of raw materials: the clay, enamels, gold and so on. The Lygo letters show that even towards the close of the eigthteenth century the factory was having problems obtaining good quality material in any quantity. Lygo spends much of his time visiting possible suppliers, and sending test samples back to Derby. A particular problem was the search for fine yellow enamel and cobalt blue. The yellow enamel coming from Italy and Holland was exceptionally scarce, and was purchased two or three ounces at a time. The letters indicate very little was being imported into the country, which considering the problems in firing this difficult colour is perhaps not surprising. Lygo even considered importing yellow enamel direct from Leghorn but the high custom duty made this unviable. Many trial specimens of cobalt blue sent to the works proved unsuitable, and each batch had to be tested before purchase of the three to ten pound lot. Lygo recorded that 'the best market' for cobalt was Hull, one dealer supplied '3 or 4 forts . . . some light some dark powder blue'. Gold, silver and mercury, or 'quick', were also purchased from London 'verditers', but even these materials could be of 'indifferent' quality.

Casks of bone ash were shipped from London around the coast. The regular suppliers appears to have been a firm called Spicers, but when their newly-built kiln failed in 1791, Lygo was forced to look elsewhere commenting of his search that bone of 'good quality and not too contaminated with dirt was not easy to procure and ship in quantity'. Lygo found himself picking through 'a source of fine bones, without sheep's trotters' at Oldfield for half an hour in order to make Duesbury a trial specimen of bone ash (19 November, 1791). The showroom manager was also obliged to spend a wet day sorting out flint at Northfleet: a supply that proved difficult and expensive to transport (December, 1792).

A letter dated August 1789 concerned with shipping goods from St Austell to Hull suggests that Cornish kaolin was to be used, and in 1795 Wedgwood 'forwarded a sample of their Cornish Clay and Stone to try'. Other odd references to clay include the preparation and sieving of 'Stourbridge clay', 'Lord Dunsmore's clay sample' (January, 1796) and in references in Duesbury's biscuit kiln trials in 1790 'clay made up at Vauxhall manufactory'. A letter to Duesbury II from his wife in 1795 records 'Mr Beard has some excellent clay to show'.

Original prints or books, such as Baptiste's flowers and horses (25 November, 1790), or the *Tour to the Isle of Wight* (8 September, 1790) or *Sharpes Crests* in twelve numbers (September, 1793), were purchased for the painters and modellers to copy. There are also details in the letters regarding the comings and goings of the artists, and the actions of Lygo and his 'spies' tracking down talent in London, giving them trials before they set out to Derby some months later. Complin and Banford were two prime examples of this system in 1789. The letters also indicate that some artists spent much of their time in London rather than working in Derby, like the modellers Spängler and Rossi. Subjects that still require detective work include the special commissions and company's customers, and an appraisal of the introduction of new designs.

The 1787 French Trade Treaty and its consequences

Early in January 1787 Lygo canvassed opinion as to the proposed trade treaty with France, so strongly supported by Wedgwood, whereby duty on porcelain and earthenware was to be bilaterally reduced from 80s to 12s 6d. The Derby managers believed it would 'hurt the fine goods trade', and were to contact Turner, the Lords George and G.H. Cavendish, and Mr E. Coke of Holkam for support to oppose the treaty. The china dealer, Mr Nurnburg, indicated there was little demand in France for 'common' British porcelain for there were only two sorts of people in that country: the rich and the poor. They were also able to import the cheaper 'India China' on more favourable terms.

By November the following year Flight (of Worcester) had taken two houses in Coventry Street to turn into a retail warehouse to sell the large quantity of china Flight junior had brought from France. Derby's customers started to notice, and indicate some preference for the new French styles at this time, with, for example, a commission from Mr Fogg for a tea set to match a Sèvres cup and saucer. A Mrs Nannick asked for some blue enamel to paint French sprigs on to dessert plates (Wedgwood's blue had 'but proved very bad'), while the Duchess of Devonshire reported that the French pieces all had sockets in their saucers (3 and 19 September, 1788 respectively). On 7 June, 1789 Lygo reported on Mr Christie's three-day sale of Sèvres, and how goods sold very cheaply hoping this would 'sicken them from importing to this country'. Another sale of quality French china 'sold astonishingly low indeed' quoted Lygo (22 July, 1789) 'I should think for nearly half the price it cost in the country' at 'great deficiency by and by', yet the sales continued.

Despite the Revolution, French porcelain still flooded the English market, 'for the people in general seems to be mad after it' (25 November, 1790); 'the great importation of French china is amazing' wrote the showroom manager (10 March, 1791), and previous good sellers like *déjeuners* were no longer wanted for 'the town is quite full of French ones' (13 January, 1791). Even previously reliable customers, like the Irish dealers, were reported to have got into the habit of going over to France to buy inexpensive china. Duesbury obviously considered selling French wares in the London showroom, but Lygo suggested 'it will hurt our sale of goods with the trade' (2 December, 1790).

The Derby factory was forced to imitate or directly copy Sèvres shapes and patterns. Lygo asked for sketches to be drawn by the modeller Catherine of Sèvres figures at Christie's salerooms, and purchased odd, even broken, pieces or borrowed china to copy or keep for comparison at the showroom. Such inspiration is very obvious on many Billingsley examples of the period. Yet even with the declaration of war in February 1793 French wares and styles dominated fashionable tablewares. Lygo frequently compared Derby products with French pieces, for example on 18 February, 1795 he wrote that their tureens were the 'best shapes about', while a Derby set decorated with insects was 'very ill done to what the French ones are' (22 May, 1794). French services remained cheap for the warehouse was able to employ enamellers, presumably refugees, at only 30 to 35 shillings a week — whom Lygo regarded as 'indifferent hands' (20 February, 1795). Derby must have frequently lost orders to the French, due to their high prices and tardy delivery. A special armorial service for Sir Frank Ford seems to have been placed with the cheaper French source after Derby produced a fine sample plate but it was 'too long in hand' (28 March, 1794), and that same spring Mrs Fitzherbert appears to have rejected a number of special plates in favour of a French product. One of the best documented and slowest table services produced by Derby was for the Margravine of Ansbach which took over eighteen months to be completed (the sample plate was requested to be delivered on 26 April, 1792 and the service which was entered in the Sales Ledger, Vol. 3, on the 15 May, 1792, was still being expected on 18 September, the following year); a French service was lent to her on at least one occasion in compensation!

Trade alternatives after c.1787

Duesbury asked Lygo to investigate the potential of other markets including Spain, where duties were high, and smuggling via their West Indian connections had been common (26 January, 1787; 23 October and 3 November, 1788). It was considered that the Italian dealer Micali could forge links for Derby in Leghorn, as Wedgwood had done (17 January, 1787), while Duesbury gained letters of introduction to the Portuguese envoys to the Hague and Denmark (14 September, 1789, Chelsea/Derby Documents, Vol. III in the British Museum). From 1792 the war against the French in Europe resulted in trade restrictions and the impounding of goods, however the vociferous Wedgwood and his supporters succeeded in pressing for a commercial treaty with Saxony, which was unsuccessfully opposed in March by Duesbury and Lygo as being 'very injurious to the china manufactories'. In fact the freedom to allow 'the importation of Saxon and other china' must have had considerably less effect on the Derby Works than the French treaty. Lygo only subsequently mentions Germanic porcelain on one occasion, when he ask for the landscapes from four Berlin comports to be copies upon a pair of Derby icepails (24 December, 1792). The period when Meissen influenced Derby porcelains to any great extent remained the early pre-Chelsea era of the 1750s and 60s.

At this time Liverpool businessmen also sought to press for the abolition of the East India Company's monopoly, and the Derby management were advised against pressing for free trade with the East (15 December, 1792 and 4 February, 1793). The East India Company's commercial power obviously did effect the Derby factory directly, for example in March 1795 Lygo was unable to acquire smalts (a cobalt mineral) for at least two to three months for the company had purchased all stocks available for shipment to China.

EXPERIMENTATION

Duesbury I and Chelsea-Derby

One only has to view the early Derby wares of the 1756-1770 and Chelsea-Derby periods to see the great strides Duesbury I made in porcelain production, creating a strong body capable of consistent, and sophisticated, modelling for figures and vases. Changes, like the introduction of soapstone in the 1760s or the acquisition of the bone-ash recipes of Chelsea, are equally a testament to the elder Duesbury's abilities. But unfortunately very little documentary evidence survives relating to technical details or materials before 1785. There is an undated recipe that would 'glaze the Chelsea ware better than any we have troid yet pray let them keep it by it self for that purpose'. References to Derbyshire woods and the transport of local lime are noted in the early factory accounts, but deliveries of clay, bone ash, gold and silver from London are exceedingly rarely recorded in the surviving 'Duesbury Papers'.

Duesbury II's experiments

Far more can be discovered about the younger Duesbury's contribution to this field of development. Science and the technological aspect of the China Works were obviously Duesbury II's great love; and Lygo sent him various publications relating to this, such as two volumes of *Watson's Chemistry* (23 July, 1789), Nicholson's *First Principles of Chemistry,* and geology books. It is certain that Duesbury read current scientific observations in the *Philosophical Transactions* too, for he quotes from such sources in his letters to Lygo.

From the late summer of 1789 Duesbury spent much of his time and energy experimenting with the kilns at Derby. Various orders were placed with local foundries relating to the casting of metal flue plates, and cylinders to be 'heated to a full red heat six times a week'. Unfortunately today's researcher shares a problem in common with the eighteenth century suppliers, and Duesbury had to apologise for the 'inability to read my bad writing' (7 January, 1790). All the small number of surviving documents in the young proprietor's hand are exceedingly difficult to read and understand. The backs of various Lygo letters dated *c.*1790 and scraps of paper have sketches of pyrometers and kiln technology, with one doodle being annotated 'original machine'. An agreement dated 24 November, 1790, required the kiln-man, Jacob Spooner (who in 1796 accompanied Billingsley to Pinxton), to swear not to divulge anything of the 'construction or use of a machine invented by W. Duesbury intended to exhibit the contraction of earthen body's when in the fire'.

During May 1790 Duesbury asked John Hancock to glean information from the Wedgwood factory relating to their saggars and firing routine; he particularly wished to learn of the composition of the saggar clay, and whether bone ash was used in the recipe. Hancock's sources were unable to help Duesbury, but thought a gift to the saggar-maker might prove fruitful. Hancock did however record the average life of a Wedgwood saggar as being between six and seven years, and that this reduced the number of saggar-makers employed by half. He also indicated that the kilns were made of 'bricks the same matter as they make the saggar with only not so nice in the tempering' laid 'looser than common building' but 'not careful vere side or not'. Certainly by December 1790 the Derby factory itself was using 'bone dust . . . in the composition of the cases in which we burn our porcelain' (from a letter from Duesbury to Messrs. Cope and Biddle, Birmingham, 23 December, 1790, asking for four tons of bone ash 'as free of filth of any kind').

In November and December 1790 Duesbury test-fired large quantities of porcelain including hundreds of dozens of small boy figures, many destined for export by Mr Williams, 'biscuited in glaze kiln'. Experiments appear to have been hampered by problems of discolouration and smoke damage, despite using wood from three different suppliers. On 30 November that year Duesbury wrote to Lygo that 'I must build a large biscuit kiln immediately.' That winter a fireman in London, apparently with Coade Stone connections, test-fired pieces of Derby in the hope that success would result in his building new kilns for Duesbury. During this period new supplies of clay are pursued, with references to Richard Bradley in London (17 November), quoting a recipe for a clay mixture (this letter is annotated on the outside 'Stourbridge Clay'), and for 'trial pieces of clay made up at Vauxhall Manufactory' (30 November). Unfortunately the results of these trials are sketchily recorded, except when a good customer like Mr Williams, has to be kept sweet with an extra 2½% discount due to drastic losses in firing; Vulliamy was distressed for want of his figures, and complained of 'roughness and blistering' in the biscuit drapery (3 February, 1791). One very muddled note survives dated 19 December, 1790 which records how boy models were dried for a week in a stove and subsequently placed and turned for no more than an hour on a far hotter plate. These figures were then placed in a saggar with 'common boys' apparently in a glaze kiln, their various weights were recorded before and after firing. This surely records an attempt to solve the problem of biscuit-firing pieces alongside previously fired glazed wares.

It was also surprising to learn that the biscuit figures used by Mr Catherine in his 'ornaments' could be re-fired to 'shrink' them to fit their brass supports if necessary (3 December, 1788).

Surviving documents and the Lygo letters indicate that trials continued, testing new materials and supplies. It is obviously no coincidence that the 'flying' (ie breaking) pot accidents generally date to immediately prior to this era of experimentation, and Duesbury's desire to make a new utilitarian body. However progress was slow and inconsistent, and though the results can be witnessed in the fine biscuit figures of the Kean period. In March 1793 the biscuit kiln was still liable to produce 'ware very much flamed and smoked' due to a coal firing. The fact that Charles King wrote to Duesbury on holiday in August 1795 about another good biscuit and glaze firing indicates something of the unpredictability of the kilns. On 2 January, 1796, further success was recorded with an agreement between John Musgrove and Duesbury and Keen to keep secret 'tryals of the biscuit kiln', by which smoked-glass spectacles enabled the fireman to distinguish the pieces while still in the safety of the hot kiln, thus eliminating the necessity of damaging rapid cooling to view the test items.

THE DECLINE OF THE DUESBURY ERA

Information as to Duesbury II's character is gleaned from letters. He was not a particularly pleasant man, nor a strong leader of men nor a good manager: factors of importance in such troubled times with huge competition from French china and the pending consequences of war. Duesbury's letters to his own sister have a high moral tone; while he all but abandons his drunken and debt-ridden younger brother, James, to Joseph Lygo, who gives him his own clothes and money and a roof over his head. Towards the mid 1790s Lygo's requests to Derby for urgent business information or goods are misinterpreted or totally ignored, and his patience is obviously sorely tried. It is Lygo in 1793 who notices a huge discrepancy in the amount of gold sent to Derby and the value of goods returned to London, and prompts an investigation into the possible fraud. The factory employees also are upset by Duesbury's changes in the 1790s, with some like Boreman deciding eventually to leave. Unfortunately there is no record as to the cause of Duesbury's failing health, and death in 1797, but it might have some bearing on his behaviour. The summer of 1795 was troubled; in the factory 'everything goes on peacefully but not with that propriety and dispatch which a good overlooker might be the means of' wrote King to Duesbury who was holidaying in Cumbria, and he went on to say 'the necessity of your presence in this critical situation of affairs' was required. In December 1795 the partnership with the little known Kean is announced, and there appear to be no more letters from Lygo to Derby dated after January the following year.

The Early Years

It is probably true to say that when people think of the early period of the Derby China Factory, they automatically think of William Duesbury and assume that the famous Derby Porcelain Factory was started by him. Porcelain was, however, first produced in Derby several years before he took over the management, though lack of documentary evidence prevents us from knowing exactly when this started or the exact site of the manufactory and even the wares produced.

The first reference to the China Works, printed in Drewry's *Derby Mercury* for the week beginning Friday, 26 January 1753, referred to the body of a drowned man 'Tis said he was one of the workmen belonging to the China Works near Mary Bridge', but there is no published map of this date which would indicate the site of the factory, though it seems probable that it occupied the same site as that later taken over and greatly expanded by William Duesbury.

This early factory must have been built on leased land, something confirmed by the press announcement dated 30 July 1756, stating that the freehold was 'TO BE SOLD' and also informs us that it was at that time occupied by Mr Heath and Company, in the China Manufactory and 'Let at £10.0.0 per annum', and that the estate consisted of seven houses and a barn, though it should be noted that there is no mention of a kiln on the site. The property was re-advertised 'for sale by auction' on 25 October, and from a later conveyance dated 1 August 1780, it can be seen that the properties had passed from Mr Charles Sheperdson of Kings Newton, his wife, Mary, and Thomas Godkin of Melbourne, to John Heath and Company on 19 November 1756. It also shows that in the previous April, when Duesbury I took over the management, a number of other adjacent plots had been acquired by Heath, and that dwelling houses had been converted into workshops and were in use in the making of china.

Prior to this date, Heath had been connected with the Pot Works at Cockpit Hill in Derby and was a signatory to the Partnership Agreement dated 11 November 1751, and another bearing the date 25 December 1753, and was still actively involved and engaged in the pottery business (and other work including banking), when on 1 January 1756, the Articles of Agreement were drawn up between himself, Andrew Planché, 'China Maker', and William Duesbury, 'Enamellor' (sic). Unfortunately this copy, which is the only one to have survived, was not signed by any of the partners, but it is of particular interest because it is the first time that William Duesbury's name is mentioned in connection with his being resident in Derby despite his earlier connection with the town. In his *London Account Book*[1] there are references to 'Darbay Figars and Darbayshire Sesen' which were sent to him during the period 1751-53 to be decorated. We do not know, however, what prompted him to move to Derby, after first moving from London to work at Longton Hall.

Jewitt states that Andrew Planché, the other partner, was in Derby for eight years[2] and Twitchett[3] quotes entries for the baptism of his children at St Alkmund's, Derby, between 1751 and 1756. But there is no further mention of his name amongst the paper preserved at Derby. In 1800 he is listed in the *Bath Directory* as Andrew Planché Floor, the English translation of his name, with the trade of dyer. He was buried in St James' Church, Bath, on 10 January 1805.

Twitchett[4] refers to the marriage of one James Marchand, of St Anne's Westminster, to Mary Oldfield of Derby at St Alkmund's on 18 June 1752, where he is described as a potter, and goes on to suggest that he may have been helping Planché at the China Works near Mary Bridge; though he could have been engaged at the Pot Works on Cockpit Hill. However, the entry in the Marriage Register of St Werburgh's, Derby, recording the marriage of William Whitehall to Bridget Lakin on 3 June 1754, is careful to describe him as 'labourer at the China House'.

The question of where Planché first learnt about china making remains unanswered. Tracing the background of the Planché family history has proved difficult because of the different ways of spelling the surname. In the Public Record Office it is spelt 'Blanchet', but even this changes with the baptism of each of his parents' children. Endré Blanchet was born on 14 March 1727/8 (o.s.) and was baptised in the Huguenot Chapel in Rider Court, London, on 24 March. He was the son of Paul Blanchet, a coffee merchant, and Marianne (née Fournier). On 30 July 1740 he was apprenticed to Edward Mounteney, a manufacturing jeweller, of Foster Lane, London, for the term of seven years. It is interesting to note that his bold clear signature 'Andrew Planché' on the document indicated that by the time he had anglicised his Christian name whilst still retaining the Huguenot family name. Due to the fact that the records are missing, it is not known if he completed the full term of his apprenticeship, though there is no reason to doubt that he gained his Freedom on 30 July 1747, because on 22 September of that year, he married Sarah Stone at St Pancras, London. Then follows a blank in our knowledge of his movements until the baptism of his son, Paul Edmund, at St Alkmund's, Derby, on 21 September 1751, and if this were his eldest child, as is thought, where was he during those intervening four years?

Twitchett,[5] again quoting Jewitt, thinks that he may have gone abroad, visiting Meissen, where he would have seen the porcelain works, and even tried to work there. But the art of porcelain making was always a closely guarded secret and at that date the journey to Saxony would have been difficult. If he did travel on the Continent, a more likely place for someone of French origin would surely have been Chantilly, where *pâte tendre* (soft paste) was being made. However, Rice[6] suggests that he could have gained his knowledge either from Thomas Briand, also of Huguenot stock, or from Nicholas Crisp, who lived in the parish of St Anne, Soho. If he were still residing in England during this period, and presumably living with his wife, why were there no children recorded before they moved to Derby. At that date he would have been only 23 years old and one must wonder if he could have gained sufficient knowledge to set up on his own as a potter, let alone possess the capital required to start the business.

Part of the answer may lie in the statement 'There is a Bourbon legend, related by the head of the Australian branch of that family, that an illegitimate son of Louis-Henri de Bourbon, Le Prince de Condé, was in Derby helping Planché set up the works. According to Tardy, Letters Patent were obtained by Chantilly under the Prince, in 1735'.[7] The legend goes on to state that by the late 1750s the Prince's son had left Derby and had purchased land at Hengoed, near Gobowan in Shropshire. Planché's mother may have been related to Louis Fournier, listed by Tardy as working at Chantilly *c.*1752, and this connection may have prompted Planché to visit Chantilly where he could have struck up a friendship with the Prince's son and when the latter moved from Derby to Shropshire, gone there with him before moving on later to Bath.

If it is accepted that the three small cream jugs[8] with the moulded strawberries applied just above the footrim, were all made at Derby, these would seem to pre-date Planché's arrival. These jugs, with different incised marks, one in the British Museum (1923, 3-18, 10) incised 'D'; another in the Victoria & Albert Museum (C.629-1920) incised 'D' over '1750'; and a third at Colonial Williamsburg, incised 'Derby', are all of a relatively high standard of workmanship and would seem to indicate proficiency rather than early experimentation.

The question then arises, where in Derby could they have been made? It has been suggested that they could possibly have been made at Cockpit Hill, but the first Agreement between the Partners setting up the Pot Works was dated November 1751 and is therefore too late. Also, the fact that they were engaged in the production of saltglaze, and later creamware, has caused other writers to reject this theory and apart from putting forward the claim of the Nottingham Road site, have left the matter open.

Another suggestion has been that the small porcelain pieces, including cats, dogs, sheep and small ornamental toys and these jugs, were fired in a pipe maker's kiln belonging to Woodward in Lodge Lane, Derby, and it was this pipe kiln that Bemrose[9] claimed to have discovered. However Williamson[10] demonstrated beyond doubt that this oven had been constructed with nineteenth century bricks. But as Rice[11] pointed out, the pieces could have been fired at Benjamin Strong's pipe kiln, which was situated nearby at Willow Road, though both these sites are some distance from Mary Bridge.

The area surrounding the Nottingham Road site is shortly to be redeveloped and it will be interesting to see if any shards relating to this early period are uncovered. If so this would contradict Salt's statement:[12] 'If there is one thing more certain than another in the history of china making in Derby it is that the Nottingham Road factory was not the original place of manufacture'.

Further uncertainty as to the date when potting first commenced is cast by Josiah Wedgwood[13] writing to Thomas Bentley on New Year's Day, 1775, stating that he had been interrupted by the visit of a man called Homes who said that he had worked at the Derby China Works for 28 years, which would imply that the factory commenced some time in 1747. An even earlier date — 1745 — is given by Chaffers[14] quoting William Locker (1797-1859) who started work at the Nottingham Road factory in 1809, stating that work had been begun about 1745 by a foreigner, in very poor circumstances, living in Lodge Lane. However, it should be remembered that Locker was quoting from memory many years later; it was Jewitt who put forward the suggestion that the foreigner referred to was Andrew Planché.

The auction sale of Derby Porcelain held at 54 Richmond Wells, Surrey, on 15 June 1756, first mentioned by Hyam in 1926 and since repeated by many writers, has been presumed to be the first such sale. But the advertisement in *The Daily News* quoted by Valpy,[16] would seem to indicate that Derby porcelain was being offered at auction in 1754:

1, 2, March, 1754
To be SOLD,
On Monday next, and the following Days
at Brook-House in Brook-Street, Holborn,
PORCELAIN Ware, of Derby manufacture consisting
of a curious Parcel, both useful and ornamental.

It is clear from this announcement, and the extensive list of items quoted by Edward Hyam[17] which were auctioned in June 1756, that porcelain was being produced at Derby some time before the date of the unsigned agreement mentioned earlier. Other sales were held by Mr Christie in London in December 1756; two in 1757; and four in 1758.

We know that shortly after taking over as manager in 1756, Duesbury set about expanding the original factory but in order to be able to meet demand and produce sufficient pieces for the auction sale in June 1756, he would have been forced to use many of the moulds that pre-dated his arrival, and no doubt the 1754 sale would have included many pieces similar to the ones sent to him earlier to decorate in his London establishment. It is also probable that any stock which he considered 'old fashioned' would have been disposed of by being included in the sales. Based on his earlier knowledge and the experience gained whilst working in London, Duesbury would have been fully conversant with the requirements of the fashionable nobility and gentry and it was of the utmost importance for him to meet these demands if he were to make them believe that his new factory at Derby was a second Dresden, as he was later to claim.

1. MacAlister, 1931, William Duesbury's *London Account Book 1751-1753*, E.P.C., Monograph, London.
2. Jewitt, 1883, *The Ceramic Art of Great Britain*, London.
3. Twitchett, 1980, *Derby Porcelain*, London, p.23.
4. Twitchett, 1980, *op. cit.*, p.23.
5. Twitchett, 1980, *op. cit.*, p.21.
6. Rice, 1983, *Derby Porcelain The Golden Years 1750-1770*, Newton Abbot, p.20.
7. Twitchett, 1987, *Wm. Duesbury. A Man of Achievement, Ceramics* Vol.V., p.72.
8. Rice, 1983, *op. cit.*, Ill. 36, p.94.
9. Bemrose, 1898, *Bow, Chelsea and Derb Porcelain*, Derby, p.104, 105.
10. Williamson, 1927, *Connoisseur*, April, pp.228-9.
11. Rice, 1983, *op. cit.*, p.15.
12. Salt, 1971, Derbyshire Archaeological Society. Research Group Newsletter No.19, July.
13. Letters of Josiah Wedgwood 1762-95. Keele University.
14. Chaffers, 8th Ed.1897, *Marks and Monograms on Pottery and Porcelain*, p.790.
15. Hyam, 1926, *The Early Period of Derby Porcelain*.
16. Valpy, 1983, *Extracts from the Daily Advertiser, 17445-1756*, E.C.C., Trans. Vol.11, Pt.3, p.205.
17. Hyam, 1926, *op. cit.*

Animals and Birds

Derby produced a considerable number of animal and bird models over the years, most of them in pairs. The first was the Boar (Fig. 1) which dates from the 'dry-edge' period and is derived from a bronze model from the workshop of Giovanni Francesco Susini (d. 1644) after a classical example, (the full-size marble sculpture in the Uffizi, Florence) though the Derby model differs from the Antique in that the head is turned more sharply and acorns have been added to the mound base. Whereas the pair illustrated here have been left 'in the white', the boars mentioned in Duesbury's *London Account Book* under the date 27 October 1752, would have been decorated, as are a pair in the British Museum. Models in a slightly smaller size were produced after Duesbury I took over the management of the factory, though the model recently found by Pamela Rowan relates to this larger size. Derby also made a running boar, perhaps an original model.

The Bull (Fig. 2) is derived from a Meissen example which in turn was based on an engraving by Johann Elias Ridinger, published in Augsburg in 1738. This too was re-issued by Duesbury slightly reduced. The Bull is decorated in enamel colours but would also have been available in 'white'. The model for the larger version was also found by Pamela Rowan at Stoke-on-Trent. In spite of some of the detail being obscured by the glaze, it is still possible, when examining the original model, to admire the skill of the modeller in depicting the movement of these animals and the detail of the body texture.

Lambs and sheep are also mentioned in Duesbury's *London Account Book* and as stated above (p. 28) it has for many years been thought that small animals and ornamental toys were fired in a pipe kiln in Derby. This example (Fig. 4) is without the usual mound base and it has therefore been thought that it was intended for a wood or *ormolu* mount. It too was based on a Meissen example, and Derby copies are now exceedingly rare. Squirrels nibbling nuts (Fig. 6), which could be placed on the dining table when the dessert was set out, were popular and were produced both at Chelsea and at Derby with only minor differences between the two versions. In the *London Account Book* dated 22 May 1751 they are described as 'marrowmots'.

The Stag and Doe at Lodge (Fig. 7) were not produced at Derby until after Duesbury's arrival, as is confirmed by the 'patch marks' on the base. These, no doubt, were produced to satisfy local pride, for the 'Stag at Lodge' was the old crest of the town and was printed as a crest and set under the heading of Drewry's *Derby Mercury*.

In the 18th century song birds were often kept in a cage, and were therefore natural subjects. The models would often seem to have been based on engravings, rather than copied from nature, as some of the models are depicted with strange colours and markings. Although some of the larger birds are easy to recognise, this is not always possible with the smaller birds like finches, and the canaries

(Fig.3) are so called mainly because of their yellow colour rather than their shape. Most of the birds were produced during the 'patch mark' period, but one bird, possibly some sort of finch, has been recorded[1] with a screw-hole in the base, which may place it in the 'dry-edge' period, though the colours used suggest that it may have been decorated somewhat later.[2]

1. Rice, 1983, *Derby Porcelain The Golden Years 1750-1770* p.46
2. The Lady Ludlow Porcelain Collection at Luton Hoo includes certain Derby specimens and these, together with others are illustrated in Rice, 1983, *op. cit.*, Illus. 68-74

1.   SEATED BOAR (one of a pair)   *c.*1751-53

The animal is seated to its right on its hind legs, with its head turned fiercely towards the spectator. On an oval mound base ornamented with oak leaves and acorns.

The torso model of the boar, together with the four legs were recently found by Pamela Rowan amongst the Derby moulds at Messrs Copelands, Stoke-on-Trent.

White glaze with 'dry-edge'.

H. 11.7cm   Derby Museum & Art Gallery (279-1955)

Lit: William Duesbury's *London Account Book 1751-1753* lists:- '1752/October 27/Mr. Michill/1 pr. Boars 5s 0d.' (MacAlister, 1931, E.P.C.)

Rackham, 1923, *Catalogue of the Herbert Allen Collection of English Porcelain*, London. Pl.1, listed as Bow. (Victoria & Albert Museum C.166-1935).

Blunt (Ed.) 1924, *The Cheyne Book of Chelsea China and Pottery*, London. Pl.2, p.57.

MacAlister, 1929, *The early work of Planché and Duesbury*, Trans. E.P.C., No.II, p.57.

Stoner, 1955, *Chelsea, Bow and Derby Porcelain Figures*, Newport Pl.45.

Hackenbroch, 1957, *Chelsea and Other English Porcelain, Pottery and Enamel in the Urwin Untermeyer Collection*, Cambridge, Mass. Pl.104, Fig.279 for similar pair.

Gilhespy, 1965, *Derby Porcelain*, London Pl.4(BM 1-28,29).

Spero, 1970, *The Price Guide to 18th Century English Porcelain*, Woodbridge, p.421 for similar pair.

Barrett & Thorpe, 1971, *Derby Porcelain*, London pps. 10 & 197, Pls. 18 & 19.

Bradley (Ed.) 1978, *Ceramics of Derbyshire 1750-1975*, Tiverton, Pl.7, p.10.

Twitchett, 1980, *Derby Porcelain*, London. Pl.14.

Bradshaw, 1981, *Eighteenth Century English Porcelain Figures, 1745-1793*, Woodbridge. Pl.171.

Rice, 1983, *Derby Porcelain, The Golden Years 1750-1770*, Newton Abbot. Pl.27.

Dawson, 1987, *Eighteenth Century English Porcelain from the British Museum*, London. Pl.38, p.33.

Rowan, 1988, *Derby Models Rediscovered*, Antique Dealer and Collectors Guide, May p.56.

2. CHARGING BULL (one of a pair)   *c.*1751-53

Figure of a bull scratching its near foreleg, with its long tufted tail arched over its back. Standing on an oval mound base. Painted in enamel colours, with the bull in a mixture of manganese and iron-red and naturalistic hues for the flowers and herbage on the base. Derived from a Meissen example, after an engraving by Johann Elias Ridinger published in Augsburg in 1738.

The model for this figure was found by Pamela Rowan (see Fig. 1) Examples in the 'white' have been recorded and the enamel decoration may have been added at a slightly later date.

'Dry-edge'. A small vent hole in the base.

H. 13 cm. L. 13 cm.   Derby Museum & Art Gallery (234-1954)

See: Royal Crown Derby Museum and Boston Museum of Fine Arts for examples of the *c.*1758 re-issued version L. 6 cm.

Lit: Stoner, 1955, *op. cit.*, Pl. 43.

Hackenbroch, 1957, *op. cit.*, p. 208, Pl. 104, Fig. 278 for another pair. (Metropolitan Museum, N.Y. 64.101. 748/9).

Gilhespy, 1965, *op. cit.*, Pl. 7 for this and its matching pair; also Pl. 151, for later version, facing left.

Barrett & Thorpe, 1971, *op. cit.*, Pl.20, pps.11 & 198.

Twitchett, 1980, *op. cit.*, Pl.12 for smaller version *c.*1758, with legs in a slightly different position.

Rowan, 1988, *op. cit.*, p.57.

Lit: Blunt, 1924, *op. cit.*, Pl.5, No.6, Fig.7 as Chelsea.

Gardner, 1943, *Birds, Beasts and Fishes, Antique Collector,* January/February, p.11.

Williams, 1973, *Early Derby Porcelain,* Exhibition Catalogue, London. No.56 for pair of finches, in similar position.

Rice, 1983, *op. cit.,* Pl.73b.

Jackson, 1988, *The Dynamic Brilliance of Derby Porcelain,* Exhibition Catalogue Brackley, Northants. Item 19.

3.   CANARIES   *c.*1760

A cock and hen canary, each perched on the 'T' branch of a tree stump covered with scattered flowers, moulded in relief. The cock bird, with its head turned sharply to its right, looking at the spectator with its left eye; the hen bird turned to its left viewing the spectator full face. Painted in naturalistic enamel colours.

Mark: Patch marks.

Cock H. 15.5 cm. Hen H. 14.8 cm.   Private Collection.

4. LAMB   *c.*1756

Recumbent lamb looking up with an alert expression. Painted in enamel colours with russet markings on the coat and the mouth, nostrils and the shape of the eyes outlined in iron-red, with the hooves and eyes black.

Copied from a Meissen example, and being without a base, was probably intended for a wood or *ormolu* mount. Recumbent lambs, with heads in slightly different positions, were also produced at Chelsea with the Red Anchor mark.

'Dry-edge'

L. 7 cm.   Private Collection.

See: Victoria & Albert Museum (Schr.1.208) also the Jones Collection. (833/4.1882)

Lit: Duesbury's *London Account Books* '1752/ May/ 1pr. ships 0. 2s. 0d.'

Gilhespy, 1965, *op. cit.*, Pl.6 for standing sheep.

Rice, 1983, *op. cit.*, Pl.31 for pair of standing sheep.

Dawson, 1988, *The F. Howard Paget Collection* DPIS Newsletter, No.11, January, p.12 for recumbent sheep.

See: Victoria & Albert Museum (C.1381 & 1382 – 1924) for pair in different posture.

Lit: Gilhespy, 1965, *op. cit.*, Pl.54 for pair in slightly different posture.

Twitchett, 1980, *op. cit.*, Pl.91.

Rice, 1983, *op. cit.*, Pl.76.

5. LEOPARD   *c.*1760

Leopard with its head turned sharply to its right, with its body supported on a tree stump, left foreleg raised and its tail tucked between its hind legs. Standing on a shaped oval base ornamented with moulded flowers. Painted in naturalistic enamel colours of creamy-yellow and black on the animal and the flowers picked out in red and yellow with green leaves.

H. 8 cm. L. 11.5 cm   Derby Museum & Art Gallery (387-2-1959)

6. SQUIRREL   *c.1760*

Squirrel crouching on its haunches, with small pricked-up ears and bushy tail curled over its back, holding a nut between its fore-paws. Set on a low mound base encrusted with fallen leaves. Painted in naturalistic brown enamel colours.

Mark: Incised '2'.

H. 9 cm.   Derby Museum & Art Gallery (332)

See: Victoria & Albert Museum (Schr.1.364) for later 1780 version.

Lit: Duesbury's *London Account Books,* 1751, '22 May 1751 – 1 pr. Marrow-mots 0. 2s. 6d'.

Christie Sale, 1756, tenth day, Thurs. 8 April, – Lot. 39. 'Two fine figures of mermots'.

Hobson, 1905, *Catalogue of English Porcelain in the British Museum,* London. Pl.29, No.7.

King, 1929, '*For the Connoisseur English Porcelain at the British Museum. 1. Early Derby*', *Country Life,* Vol.LXV, January, p.99. for uncoloured example.

Trans. E.C.C., 1934, No.2, Pl.XIX, p.44 Coloured example in private collection.

Austin (Ed.) 1977, *Chelsea Porcelain at Williamsburg,* Williamsburg, Va. Pl.104.

Twitchett, 1980, *op. cit.,* Pl.72.

Adams, 1987, *Chelsea Porcelain,* London, Pl.25 for Chelsea example.

Dawson, 1987, *op. cit.,* Pl.2 for Chelsea example in British Museum (Porc. Cat. II 7).

Lit: Spero, 1970, *op. cit.*, p.422, for example without stump.

Barrett & Thorpe, 1971, *op. cit.*, Pl.21 without bocage.

Twitchett, 1980, *op. cit.*, Pl.71 with bocage added.

7. DOE AT LODGE (one of a pair)   *c.*1760

A doe crouching on the ground with her front legs bent backwards under her body and her head turned to her left, looking towards the spectator, with an alert expression. Set in front of a flowering tree stump and scattered flowers on a low mound. Painted in naturalistic enamel colours. Issued as a pair to the Stag at Lodge.

Mark: Patch marks

H. 11 cm. L. 10.5 cm.   Derby Museum & Art Gallery (321)

A Stag at Lodge was the old crest of Derby and was known locally as 'The Buck in the Park'.

Early Wares of the 'Dry-Edge' Period

Robin Barkla

In an attempt to prevent the glaze from running under the base during the firing, figures and other wares were held upside down in the liquid glaze and were either not completely immersed, or the lower edge of the base was wiped clean after dipping. If these precautions proved unsuccessful, the base was then ground flat, a time-consuming operation. The dry edge of unglazed paste can also be seen on the 'snowmen' figures produced at Longton Hall at about the same date.

There are about twelve models of useful domestic wares from the 'dry-edge' period that have been recorded and, in some cases, only one example is known to exist. These include the three cream jugs referred to on page 28, and it is now thought that the fluted cup with sprigged and moulded decoration, illustrated in Bradley[1] and three coffee cups in the Victoria & Albert Museum[2] belong to this group.

Marine themes were also popular on the dining table, and sweetmeat dishes in the form of three shells resting on a base composed of coral and rocks and a large single shell for salt were produced. Sauceboats in the form of a large, deep, fluted shell with a crayfish and a seaweed loop handle were made with all the shells realistically portrayed, even the tiny ones, and this careful replication was continued into the Duesbury years with the small shells around the bases of the 'dry-edge' figure of Neptune with a dolphin.

Other popular models were based on the theme of garden produce and a tureen moulded in the form of a cabbage could be set beside another tureen representing a partridge sitting on its nest (Fig.8). This fashion started when J.J. Kändler made a model for one in 1741, which was produced at Meissen, and the idea was then taken up at Chelsea, Bow and Worcester.

1. Bradley, 1978, *op. cit* pl.453
2. Victoria & Albert Museum Nos. C.1045–1924, 302–1916 and 824–1956. A small sauceboat (C.61–1967) also belongs to this group.

See: Victoria & Albert Museum (Schr.1.64) for Bow example, on a slightly different shaped stand.

Lit: Rackham, 1923, *op. cit.*, No.65, Pl.12, listed as Chelsea.

Williams, 1975, *Eighteenth Century European White Porcelain,* Burlington House Fair, Exhibition Catalogue. No. 21, white, without stand (L. 12.5 cm.)

Bradley, 1978, *op. cit.*, Pl.94, for pair of turtle doves.

Twitchett, 1980, *op. cit.*, Pl.93 for pair without stands, painted in naturalistic enamel colours (L. 11.9 cm.)

Lippert, 1987, *Eighteenth-Century English Porcelain in the Collection of the Indianapolis Museum of Art,* Indianopolis. Cat. No.2, p.63 for Chelsea partridge and Cat. No.22, p.123 for Derby pigeon; also Fig.4, p.64, for Meissen example.

8. PARTRIDGE TUREEN, COVER AND STAND *c.*1750-5

A tureen in the form of a partridge sitting on its nest, with its head turned sharply to its left. The base is modelled to represent the nest and the leaf-moulded stand, with a twisted stalk handle and frilly up-turned edge, represents the ground on which it rests.

Tureens in the form of partridges and doves were supplied in pairs. They were copied originally from a model attributed to J.J. Kändler, *c.*1741, produced at Meissen.

A slightly later version, *c.*1760, was also produced. Similar tureens were also made at Chelsea, Bow and Worcester.

Undecorated.

H. 11 cm. (including stand). Tureen L. 15.5 cm.   Private Collection.

Figures in the 'Dry-Edge' Period

Robin Barkla

The best of the early figures belonging to this early 'dry-edge' period are superbly modelled with crisp clean lines, portraying a vitality and spontaneity which typifies the spirit of the eighteenth century. Although we presume that the gifted modeller of such figures was Planché, we have little proof of this assumption: instead, therefore, of it being called the Planché period, it would be more satisfactory if it were called 'dry-edge' period, because this is one of the characteristics, resulting from production techniques, that differentiate this early period from the later ones.

The composition of the paste of the early pieces varies somewhat from that used later; it is translucent with a very close texture and is neither phosphatic nor steatitic. The high proportion of silica results in a heavy glassy body, which, under ultra-violet light, floresces a bluish-white colour. The glaze also varies considerably – sometimes it is transparent and glossy, alternatively warm and almost creamy, or fairly dull, resembling candlewax. Occasionally it is blued and at other times it contains some tin oxide, with a white, somewhat opaque, effect. It is quite often also disfigured with black specks. On some examples the glaze is fairly thick and has gathered in crevices, obscuring the modelling; whilst on others, it is close fitting. On a few examples, the glaze seems to have failed to adhere completely, resulting in areas of almost bare paste, which are sometimes oxidised.

When one considers the glassy paste used, the poses and modelling of the figures are quite ambitious, and, despite the considerable lead oxide content, they remained fairly stable in the kiln although there were often instances of kiln-sagging. The figures were usually slip-caste before firing and the base filled in, though a few examples are known where the base is not filled in. Some rare filled-in examples are known without vent holes, but usually these were made to enable the air trapped inside the figure to escape during firing. These holes vary in size and in the earliest figures are usually funnel-shaped, looking as though they were intended to receive the shank of a counter-sunk screw, though some of the holes simply have straight sides.

The typical base on which the figure is set is a simple mound which may be sparsely decorated with modelled flowers, buds and leaves. Occasionally a spray of flowers was painted on the base, as on the Flute Player of *c.*1752. Sometimes the base was given a slight rococo-style moulding, whilst on others the moulding is shell-like. The bases also get higher and are slightly scrolled; two of the larger figures, known as St Thomas and St Philip, have quite elaborately scrolled bases. As a general rule, however, it is not until the end of the 'dry-edge' period that the awareness of the rococo style becomes evident on the base.

There are over sixty 'dry-edge' models known and most of the figures typify the spirit of the eighteenth century. Many of them have holes low down at the back, so that metal branches, bearing porcelain flowers, could be added. It is known that flowers for this purpose were made at Derby, though most of the flowers that have survived seem to have been made at Vincennes. A number of the models are after Meissen figures and the Map Seller, also copied at Chelsea, closely follows the Reinicke model.

There are no known sources for the marvellously modelled chinoiserie groups, although they are similar in style to the chinoiseries of François Boucher; however the prototype could be based on the model of the Seated Man and Woman, produced by Kändler in 1735. Some of the figures in these chinoiserie groups were later repeated individually – often as Musicians – the Man with a Lute and the Woman with a Double Drum. These individual models were probably produced a short time later, as they are smaller than the group figures, and their collars and cuffs have been re-worked and they are decorated in colours used shortly after Duesbury I took over the management of the factory.

As with all the 'dry-edge' models, most examples of these groups are white. This was popular in England in the early 1750s and it shows the skilful modelling to best advantage. But there are also examples which are delicately decorated with pale washes of puce, primrose and green; and others decorated with flower sprays and sprigs, or star-shaped florets in bright colours. It should also be remembered that some figures which now appear as white, were originally painted. This can sometimes be spotted in the crevices where the non-lasting oil colours have not been rubbed away. Where enamel colours have been used, they can sometimes help as a rough guide as to the date of the figure because a new yellow was introduced c.1754–5, and at the same period gilding began to be used for the edge of garments and to draw attention to the buttons, for example see Fig.9. Often the pieces were composed of small figures used elsewhere in other ways and the small Chinese boy incorporated in the latter group had previously formed part of the set of the Elements representing 'Water'. Pocket watches at this time were rare and valuable and when not being carried on the person, were placed in a stand. This group was designed as a watch stand.

It is thought that the Lady and Servant (Fig.10), could also have originally been designed as a watch stand, but some mishap in the firing distorted the shape of the circular cut-out space. It would seem that either the idea, or possibly a model which they were attempting to copy, was more ambitious than it was possible to achieve with the paste then being used. Models of this quality must always have been expensive to produce and the fact that, in this instance, one of the arms has fallen off, probably in the firing, but had been removed before it got stuck to the base; and also that what would appear to be a shelf had collapsed, leaving the lady looking up at nothing, did not stop it from being passed out of the factory.

It seems likely that much of the decoration on these early pieces was done in Duesbury's London decorating establishment. Even though enamel painting had been practised in Germany for quite some time before porcelain began to be made in Europe, little enamel work was done in England. The early English porcelain makers may have sought advice from the few craftsmen working in enamel on silver or copper for jewellers, and certainly some Continental enamellers were employed by them in England to do this work. When one examines the Derby figures, decorated with washes and rather unimaginative designs, in a limited range of colours, one realises that the craft of enamelling was then in its infancy.

9. CHINAMAN PERCHED ON ROCKS AND A BOY
(Sorcerer and Chinese apprentice?)   *c.*1752

Chinaman with flying drapery and a conical hat, sitting perched on an elaborate rococo base with both his arms and legs outstretched, and a Chinese boy, with shaven head, squatting below him, with his right arm raised and looking upwards (left foot broken). Originally designed as a watch holder.

The faces of the two figures are painted in naturalistic enamel colours, with the florets on the magician's garment red, the under-garment sleeves and collar pale yellow, the hat painted in alternating puce and yellow stripes and the boy's jacket painted pale green. The rococo scroll base is picked out in puce and turquoise enamel, with sparse gilding. Set on a pierced rococo scroll base.

'Dry-edge'

H. 21.1 cm.   Derby Museum & Art Gallery (43-1978)

See: British Museum (Reg. No.1938, 3-14, 102) Wallace Elliot Bequest, for example without the boy. Patch marks.

Lit: Gilhespy, 1951, *Crown Derby Porcelain*, Leigh-on-Sea. Fig.140 for example complete with elaborate rococo frame for holding a watch.

Godden, 1974, *British Porcelain, an Illustrated Guide,* London. p.204, Fig.225
for example of the Chinese boy.

Bradley, 1978, *op. cit.,* Pl.4 for example of the boy, representing 'Water', in the set of the Elements.

Twitchett, 1980, *op. cit.,* Pl.8.

Bradshaw, 1981, *op. cit.,* Pl.92, p.185.

Rice, 1983, *op. cit.,* Pl.16, p.179.

Experimental and 'Transitional' Pieces

Robin Barkla

There are also a few pieces which are thought to date from the early 1750s, prior to Duesbury's arrival at Derby, which are referred to as 'experimental'. The cream jugs with incised bases seem to have been influenced by 'triangle' Chelsea and 'Girl-in-a-Swing' models; they are slipcast, neither phosphatic nor steatitic, contain lead oxide, and are decorated with slip-moulded wild strawberry flowers, which have concave petals. Most of the figures of this small experimental group are 'dry–edge' and have very similar slip decoration; they include the larger figures of Kitty Clive (which are slip cast and not phosphatic and so not made at Bow); a Pug Scratching its Ear; and a headless Actor. Some of the figures are rather stiffly modelled with the eyeballs indented and the hands too long and with very little separation between the fingers. There seems to be no doubt that these were not produced by the fine modeller of the 'dry-edge' period.

There are also a few pieces probably made *c.*1755-6, which are also thought to be experimental products of the Derby manufactory.[1] They have been called 'transitional' pieces and could have been the result of experiments aimed at achieving a paste which would allow more complicated modelling. They appear usually on pierced rococo-scroll bases, with a tendency to dirty black specks in the body.

Some of the models, like the seated pair of a Boy with a Dog and Bird, and a Girl with a Lamb,[2] are quite stiffly modelled. But others, for example the Dancing Boy,[3] wearing dainty clothes and dancing, his weight balanced on his left foot, retains much of the gracefulness seen in models of the 'dry-edge' period.

The Crested Pheasant Candlestick (Fig.11), which forms part of this group, is well modelled and attractively presented and the brownish-red of the enamel outlining the scrolls on the base is most unusual. Although this one is unmarked, other pieces have a very distinctive mark of an incised circle surrounding a triangle subdivided by lines and dots.[4] It is interesting to note that there are no known examples of these 'transitional' models produced either before or after the 1755-6 dates mentioned. Although they have been thought of as Derby, Clifford pointed out[5] that this attribution is by no means satisfactory.

In discussing the group Rice[6], rejected Arthur Lane's attribution to Derby[7] and suggested that the group should be called after the 'Girl-on-a-horse' model. Writing in 1983, before the shards excavated on the site of the Vauxhall factory had been seen, he put forward the suggestion that they might have been produced at the Vauxhall factory run by Nicholas Crisp[8].

1. Bradley (Ed.) 1978, *op. cit.* p.12.
2. Rice, 1983, *op. cit.* Pl.40.
3. Bradley, 1978, *op. cit.,* Pl.8.
4. Bradley, 1978, *op. cit.,* Pl. 8a.
5. Bradley 1978, *op. cit.,* p.12.
6. Rice, 1983, *op. cit.,* p.33.
7. Lane, 1961, *English Porcelain Figures of the Eighteenth Century,* London p.100.
8. R. Stevenson, 1989 Description of ceramic material from the Vauxhall site. Trans. E.C.C., Vol. 13, Pt.3. appendix B, p.224.

10. LADY AND SERVANT (incomplete) *c.*1756

A lady wearing a detailed flowered-pattern dress, with her head turned upwards, away from the spectator, looking over her right shoulder at an imaginary object. The servant also in a floral-patterned robe, is kneeling facing her and offering a tray of fruit. Both figures are set on a rococo scroll base. Behind the lady is what would seem to be a shelf, pierced with two small holes intended to incorporate a separate object, and a cornucopia-shaped vase at one end. In the biscuit firing, however this has fallen forward and the circular cut-out space become distorted. Also the lady's left arm has fallen off in the biscuit firing (left foot broken off). Possibly intended as a watchstand.

Probably derived from a Kändler piece, but no other examples have previously been recorded.

Painted in enamel colours with pink and blue flowers on the lady's dress, including the cavity in the lady's left shoulder where her arm should be, and a pink sash around her waist. The servant's dress is painted with roses and blue flowers and leaves. The scroll base is outlined in blue, green, yellow and red enamel with traces of gilding.

Mark: Evidence of 'patch marks' on ground-down base.

H. 20.7 cm.   Derby Museum & Art Gallery (1678-1986)

Lit: Anderson, 1986, *Two remarkable pieces of Derby Porcelain*. DPIS Newsletter No. 7, December.

Anderson, 1987, *Wm. Duesbury, father and son Men of Industry,* Museum & Art Gallery, Derby, p.28.

11. CANDLESTICK
c.1754

Candlestick in the form of a crested pheasant, with an alert expression and looking towards the spectator, resting on a stump in front of a spirally twisted support covered with flowers moulded in relief. The upper surface of the support is glazed, as if to receive an ormolu sconce, though it would appear that one was never inserted. Set on an elaborate rococo-scroll mound base.

Painted in enamel colours with yellow on the bird's breast, white neck and the wings puce shading to white, with a yellow beak and puce crest, the flowers in naturalistic enamel colours with red on the base and traces of gilding. It is thought that the enamel decoration may have been added later.

Five examples have been recorded, 3 left–hand examples and 2 right. They all belong to a distinctive group, usually on pierced rococo-scroll bases. They are of a light-weight paste with a tendency to dirty black specks in the body.

Unmarked.

19.7 cm.   Private Collection

See: Victoria & Albert Museum (C.162-1929) 'Cat up a tree' (missing, probably, a dog on the ground), which is marked with an incised circle surrounding a triangle sub-divided by lines and dots.

Museum of Art, Providence, Rhode Island (Katz Collection) for the only recorded example in 'white'.

Lit: Hackenbroch, 1957, *op. cit.*, 'Crested Pheasant' p.211, Pl.106, Fig.280.

Barrett & Thorpe, 1971, *op. cit.*, p.14, Pl.23, for example of one of a matching pair, facing opposite direction, with a small vignette, on a scroll base. (Formerly in the Eckstein and Foden Collections).

Williams, 1973, *op. cit.*, No.10 for other right hand example.

Bradley, 1978 *op. cit.*, Pl.8a, for incised mark.

Rice, 1983, *op. cit.*, Pl.42 and p.36, listing four other known examples. Also Pl.150a, for incised mark, referred to as 'Girl-on-a-horse' mark.

Useful and Decorative Wares of the 'Patch Mark' Period

Robin Barkla

During the 'patch mark' period (1756-1770) the output of the factory was considerably enlarged and wares for all sorts of different uses were produced. When being fired, the wares were placed in saggars and set on balls of clay, which resulted in dry rough 'patch' marks, and this Derby characteristic continued until *c.*1811. The wares were well decorated though the artists are usually referred to as either 'the cotton-stalk painter' or 'the moth painter' because little is known about the early artists at Derby.

From the parish records in Derby we know that when Constantine Smith married Hannah Storer on 11 July 1757, at All Saints Church, he is described as a china painter and that when William Billingsley I married Mary Dallison on 9 October, 1757, at St Werburgh's Church, he too was described as a china painter. Since both men had previously worked in London, as is known from the Rate Books of Clerkenwell and Chelsea,[1] it is probable that both men had known William Duesbury before they moved to Derby. Other painters names listed by Rice[2] include Mason (1763) Thomas Strong (1765), and Thomas Edkins (1767). The dates refer to their respective marriages and presumably all would have been youngish men at the time. Fidèle Duvivier, who may have worked at Chelsea some time between 1764-69, married Elizabeth Thomas at All Saints Church, Derby, on 4 December 1769 when he was 29 years old, and a few weeks before his marriage had signed a four-year agreement with William Duesbury which bears the date 31 October 1769. There is also another mystery name Thos. F, which is signed on the wing of a moth and is illustrated by Barrett & Thorp.[3]

The decoration on these early pieces is of a uniformly high standard and the moths and other insects are, for the most part, accurately drawn and decorated in a realistic manner, though the stems on some of the flower-decorated pieces could never have nourished let alone have supported the weight of the flowerhead.

At this time the rococo style was still popular and the two vases (Figs. 12 and 13) bear witness to this. They illustrate what Dr Colin Roth[4] describes as 'capitalising on the expressive potential of asymmetry, bringing increasingly by dramatic contrasts into more or less precarious balance'. The style was copied from an earlier design produced at Longton Hall, where Duesbury had worked for a short time before moving to Derby, and though they are described as 'vases', the flat top would seem to indicate either that they had covers, which have been lost, or, possibly that they may have served as candlesticks.

The 'parfum' vases (Fig. 14), were definitely designed with covers which were pierced to allow the perfume of the dried pot-pourri that they contained to permeate and sweeten the room. This design was copied from Meissen and similar perforated vases were also produced at other English factories at this time.

The toilet box, cover and stand, moulded in the form of a rose (Fig. 16), though possibly not made until just after Duesbury took over the factory management, could well be similar to some of the items offered in the June 1756 sale. So, too, could the peach box (Fig. 15) and the rose basket (Fig. 17), but the stand for the rose toilet box is exceedingly rare. Baskets (Fig. 18) with either pierced or solid sides, must have been in great demand and the number of different sizes of these baskets that have survived indicate the vast range of the factory's output. Sometimes these are referred to in the early factory descriptions as 'spectacle baskets', a term which baffled later generations, until it was realised that the short bridge connecting the two large circles resembled a pair of old fashioned spectacles.

Before the days of refrigeration much of the meat consumed would, by today's standards, be considered as unhygienic. Both poultry and game having been shot, were hung in a game larder before being cooked and eaten. It was therefore considered necessary, in addition to salt, to place condiments on the table, and cruet sets (Fig. 19), carefully labelled and originally set in a wooden stand, were produced. Few sets now exist and most of them have become separated from their original stand.

Ice houses were a regular feature in English gardens in the eighteenth century. These were packed with snow during the winter months so that the ice would be available for use during the warmer summer months. Ice pails were probably originally supplied in pairs and were set on the dining table in the French manner, with Sèvres *seaux à bouteilles* on the table. Ice pails of this early period (Fig. 20) are now exceedingly rare, due no doubt to careless handling. In the later period, as listed in the Sales Ledger Book,[5] double ice pails were a common extra when ordering a desert (sic) service.

1750-1770 was also a time at which the picturesque was much admired and instead of being a merely topographical record of a place, a scene depicted landscape as art decoration, and the rural scenes depicted on the inkstand (Fig. 21) were obviously intended to inspire the writer when sitting down to write. No doubt the idea of putti playing with a lamb was also intended to promote romantic notions. Writing was quite a complicated and time-consuming matter, requiring not only quill pens, but sharp blades to re-shape the writing end of the quill when it became worn, and pounce powder to dry the ink to prevent smudging.

The Pedestal stands (Fig. 22) were obviously intended to be part of a larger display, but since no complete unit has survived, one cannot be sure of their exact purpose. It has been suggested that they were intended as a socle (support) for a bust, because the upper surface was left unglazed. But the size and shape of the cut-out hole would seem to indicate that the base of the bust, or other object, needed to be kept steady. And what was the purpose of the shallow

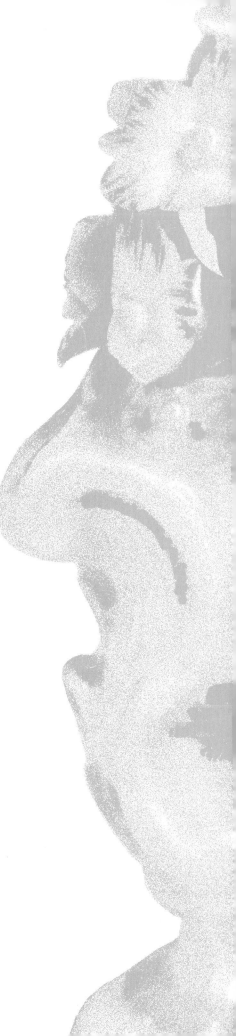

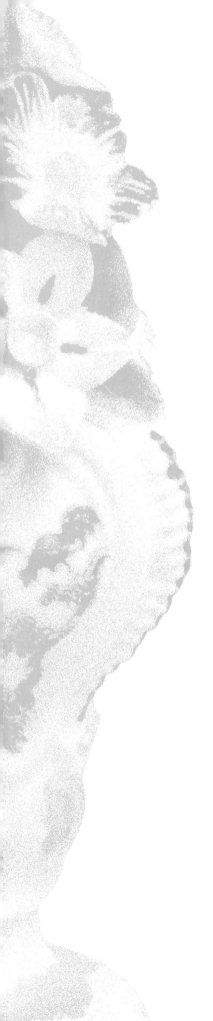

groove which was cut into the top side of the stand? Did it have some special purpose or was it purely for decoration? In which case the foot or base of the object must have been shaped to follow closely the outline shape of the stand. Certainly most busts are intended to be viewed from the front, and in support of the socle theory, most of the stands are only decorated on three sides and would therefore seem to have been intended to be placed against a wall. One stand, however, sold at auction in London in 1988, was painted on all four sides and in the canted corner angles, shaped pierced holes had been cut, making it seem that *ormolu* mounts were intended to be inserted and that the stand would have been seen in the round.

There were obviously still great difficulties that had to be overcome when glazing and firing these large pieces. Although the hollow inside surface was glazed, the top surface was unglazed and on two examples in the British Museum,[6] both suffer from cracks and bubbles in the paste, which have burst in firing.

Surprisingly no contemporary print or picture is at present known to exist which shows the manner in which wall pockets (Fig.23) were used in a domestic setting. They were supplied in pairs, but whether they were placed above the fireplace on the chimney breast, or in a drawing room, in the wall space between the windows, is uncertain. However, what is clear is that they must have been in great demand, being made in salt-glaze, tin-glaze and creamware in addition to soft paste porcelain and oriental hard paste. The oriental version was designed so that the pockets could be 'slotted on' to a pinhead in the wall which would have helped protect the wall from possible damage by water, if they were filled with fresh flowers. However it is more likely that dried flowers were used, being displayed in a more decorative manner without requiring the depth or space required if the holder were used for fresh flowers.

1. Tapp, 1939, *Thomas Hughes, First Enameller of English China, of Clerkenwell* Trans E.C.C., Vol.2, No.6.
2. Rice, 1983, *op. cit.* Pl. 138 for example in British Museum.
3. Barrett & Thorpe, 1971, *op. cit.* Pl.43.
4. Roth, 1989, *Rococo*, DPIS, Journal 1, p.56.
5. Chelsea and Derby Documents, Bemrose Collection of Papers. Vol.3. British Museum.
6. British Museum Cat. Porc.II. 46 & 47.

12. ROCOCO VASE *c.*1760

Vase formed of an asymmetrical moulded rococo scroll body, crisply moulded, with a moulded flared neck and flat top on a circular pedestal foot. Painted on one side with a crested pheasant standing on the ground and another bird in flight; and on the reverse side, with butterflies and insects and the rococo scroll work outlined in green and gilt.

Originally copied from a Longton Hall design (where William Duesbury had been working in 1755).

It has been suggested that the flat top would indicate that they were originally supplied with covers.

Mark: Patch marks.

H. 22.8 cm.   Derby Museum & Art Gallery (601-1963)

See: Victoria & Albert Museum (C.207-1935) for vase with slightly different moulding.

Lit: Bemrose, 1898, *Bow, Chelsea and Derby Porcelain,* Derby, p.152 for Longton Hall example.

Rackham, 1923, *op. cit.,* No.46, p.16 as 'probably Chelsea, though not established; they may have been made, if not at Bow, at Derby'.

Barnard, 1924, *Chats on Wedgwood Ware,* London. Pl. facing p.218, for carved wooden pattern.

Hurlbutt, 1933, *Some Vases in the Hurlbutt Collection, Connoisseur,* Vol.XCI, No.377, Jan. Pl.VII for vase and cover.

Gilhespy, 1951, *op. cit.,* Fig.97 for both large and small vases.

Watney, 1957, *Longton Hall Porcelain,* London. Pl.63a. for Longton Hall, Middle Period 1754-57.

Mallet, 1969, *Rococo English Porcelain. A Study in Style,* Apollo, Vol.XC, No.90, August. Cover, p.110 and fig.12.

Barrett & Thorpe, 1971, *op. cit.,* Pl.75. p.17.

Williams, 1973, *op. cit.,* Pl.32 for similar shape.

Gabszewicz & Freeman, 1982, *Bow Porcelain,* London. Pl.49 for Bow example of similar shape. Pl.136 as a rococo candlestick.

Rice, 1983, *op.cit.,* p.138 for example in British Museum.

Mallet, 1984, *'Rococo in English Ceramics',* Victoria & Albert Exhibition. *Rococo Art & Design in Hogarth's England.* Pl.024, p.252.

13. VASE

*c.*1760

Small vase, shaped as No.12, with large flowers moulded in relief set in the neck of the vase.

Painted in enamel colours with a scene taken from *Aesop's Fables*, depicting 'the fox and the cockerel in a tree' on one side and butterflies and insects on the reverse.

Mark: Patch marks

H. 11.5 cm.

Derby Museum & Art Gallery (770-2-1966)

See: Victoria & Albert Museum (Schr.1.315) for similar pair.

Lit: Rice, 1983, *op. cit.,* Pl.137.

14. 'PARFUM' VASE AND COVER   *c.1760*

Pear-shaped with pierced and moulded decoration, set in three equidistant sections around the pot, with a wide mouth and spreading pedestal foot; a high domed cover divided into three sections with pierced and moulded decoration and surmounted by moulded leaves and an open flower finial.

The design is copied from Meissen.

Painted in the shaped reserves, in naturalistic enamel colours, with a floral bouquet, birds and butterflies on the body and cover of the pot and around the spreading foot, and the moulded decoration picked out in pale green and puce.

Mark: Patch Marks.

H. 23 cm. (inc. cover)   Derby Museum & Art Gallery (96-1981)

Lit: Rackham, 1923, *op. cit.,* No.45, Pl.13 for Chelsea example.

Barrett & Thorpe, 1971, *op. cit.,* Pl.29, without cover.

Sandon, 1969, *The Illustrated Guide to Worcester Porcelain,* London, Pl.120 for Worcester perforated vase.

Bradley, 1978, *op. cit.,* Pl.116 for similar shape.

Rice, 1983, *op. cit.,* Pl.133a for similar shape and decoration.

15. BOX AND COVER   *c.*1760

Box moulded in the form of a peach, with a 'twig' handle on the side and an applied spray of leaves and an open flower finial on the cover. Painted in naturalistic enamel colours.

Mark: Patch marks

H. 7.5 cm.   Derby Museum & Art Gallery (421-1959)

See: Victoria & Albert Museum (C.703-1925) for example with slightly different arrangement of the leaves and flower finial.

Lit: Blunt, 1924, *op. cit.,* for Chelsea box of similar type.

Barrett & Thorpe, 1971, *op. cit.,* Pl.40.

Bradley, 1978, *op. cit.,* Pl.83.

Lit: E. Hyam, 1926, *The Early Period of Derby Porcelain*, London. Refers to a sale which took place in June 1756 at 54 Richmond Wells, Surrey, which states: 'the greatest variety of the Derby Porcelain, in Figures, Jars, Candlesticks, Sauceboats, Lettices, Leaves, Roses and several curious pieces for Desserts, finely enamelled in Dresden flowers, reckoned by Judges who have been purchasers to excel, if not exceed, anything of the Kind in England.'

Mackenna, 1951, *Chelsea Porcelain. The Red Anchor Wares,* Leigh-on-Sea. Pl.35, fig.71 for Chelsea Box.

Williams, 1973, *op. cit.,* Pl.36 for a different example, also Pl.79.

Rice, 1983, *op. cit.,* Pl.146, and p.60, where it is suggested that the 'roses' mentioned above, may be referring to a toilet box.

16. TOILET BOX, COVER AND STAND   *c.*1756-9

Box moulded in the form of a rose in full bloom, with the petals on the lower section opening slightly outwards, and with moulded petals on the cover, which is surmounted by a stalk to form a loop handle. The stand, with raised and everted rim, is also moulded to represent the petals of a rose.

Painted in naturalistic enamel colours with the petals on the box outlined in red, the stalk handle green, and a continuous chain of heart's-ease painted in the centre of the stand.

Box H. 6 cm. Stand D. 10.4 cm.   Private Collection

17.   ROSE BASKET   *c.*1760

Basket moulded as an open flower with overlapping petals and sur‐
rounded by partially overlapping leaves, with small spaces between the
leaves. Painted in naturalistic enamel colours with the petals shaded
carmine red and the leaves picked out in green and yellow with carmine
veins. The moulding of this rose basket differs from the contemporary
paeony dish.

The idea of a paeony dish was copied from a Meissen original, where a
dish, without handles, was first moulded in 1746, by J.G. Ehder, '*1
Confect Schaale in Gestalt einer Sonnen-Rose von Thon bausirt*'.

Mark: Patch marks

D. 20.2 cm.   Private Collection

Lit: R. Rückert, 1966, *Meissener Por‐
zellan 1710-1810* Exhibition Catalogue,
Munich. Pls.703 & 704 for Meissen
example.

Lit: Rackham, 1923, *op. cit.,* No.28, p.12, attributes a similar basket 'as probably Bow' but adds 'that the early productions of Derby, must be taken into account'.

Mackenna, 1972, *The F.S. Mackenna Collection of English Porcelain. Part 1, Chelsea 1743-1758,* Leigh-on-Sea. Nos. 83-86, Set of four dessert baskets, Red anchor, Chelsea.

Barrett & Thorpe, 1971, *op. cit.,* p.22, quote an announcement dated 6 March, 1758, placed in the *Public Advertiser* by Mr. Williams, the Factor of the Derby China Company at their warehouse in London: 'that he has this day unpacked the greatest Variety of new Figures from Derby… and several curious Wares in Leaves, Baskets, etc., for Desserts, finely painted in Dresden flowers, and all warranted true enamel.'

Williams, 1973, *op. cit.,* Pl.46 for similar pierced basket decorated with cherries.

Rice, 1983, *op. cit.,* Pl.113b, p.56.

18. OVAL PIERCED BASKET   *c.*1760

An oval pierced basket with cut-out sides, and double rope twist handles (one broken) terminating in flower finials, moulded on the exterior with applied florets, with rope moulding round the base.

Painted on the inside with cherries and leaves attached to a twig, surrounded by flying insects and a butterfly, the handles picked out in green, the sepals of the florets green, the rope moulding round the base yellow, and the rim outlined in brown.

Mark: Patch marks

L. 23 cm.   Derby Museum & Art Gallery (389-1959)

19. CRUET SET   *c.*1760-65

A set of five bottles, each of baluster shape, on a spreading base and contracting into a narrow neck, hidden by perforated silver caps, each stamped 'A.B' and each for a different condiment (mustard was then served in a dry, powder, state).

Painted in naturalistic enamel colours with floral sprays on each bottle and marked within a stylised foliate border 'SUGAR', 'OIL', 'MUSTARD', 'VINEGAR and 'PEPPER'.

Mark: Ground-down base

H. 14.5 cm, 12 cm, & 10.4 cm. (without mounts)
Derby Museum & Art Gallery (598-1972)

See: Victoria & Albert Museum (C.305-1926) for set in wooden stand.

Lit: Sandon, 1969, Pl.67 for Worcester dry and wet mustard pots.

Spero, 1970, *op. cit.,* p.192 for wet mustard pot.

Barrett & Thorpe, 1971, *op. cit.,* Pl.73, with different tops.

Rice, 1983, *op. cit.,* Pl.130 & p.58.

20. ICE PAILc.1760

Circular four-lobed shape with circular rim, set on a raised circular foot and two elaborate handles set just below the rim.

Painted in enamel colours on both sides with a floral bouquet including tulips and scattered insects. A gilt dentil border round the rim and the handles outlined in gilt.

Copied from Sèvres *seaux à bouteilles*.

Mark: Three patch marks on foot rim.

H. 17.3 cm.   Derby Museum & Art Gallery (907-1983)

See: Victoria & Albert Museum (C.1072-1924) for similar shape with turquoise ground decoration.

City of Manchester Art Gallery (1947-678) for similar shape decorated with moorhens and other exotic birds.

Lit: Bradley, 1978, *op. cit.*, Pl.108.

Twitchett, 1980, *op. cit.*, Pl.211 for complete Sèvres table setting showing the different sizes, also copied at Derby.

Graham & Oxley, 1981, *English Porcelain Painters*, Exhibition Catalogue, London, No.51 for later example *c.*1790, with scroll shell handles.

21. INKSTAND
*c.*1765

Comprising a pen tray moulded with three depressions for the inkpot, pounce pot and taper stick, set on a flat shaped base, with shell moulding round the edge. The cover of the quill box moulded with two putti playing with a lamb, surrounded by moulded rococo decoration. The pounce pot, squat bellied, with slightly depressed perforated top (cover missing). The inkpot of similar shape, with depressed top and circular hole cut in the centre (cover missing). The short taperstick baluster-shaped, with circular base and shaped spike to fit into small socket in the base of the stand, with everted rim round the nozzle.

The pots painted in turquoise enamel colours with oriental landscapes on two sides, set in a shaped cartouche, with a stylised floral border round the rim of the taperstick nozzle and on the inside of both pots, with shell scrolls on the base picked out in turquoise and pink.

Mark: Patch marks.

H. Taper stick on stand 7.9 cm. Stand L. 21.3 cm.
Derby Museum & Art Gallery (405-1959)

Note: Pounce powder was made from pulverised gum sandarac or cuttlefish bone, rosin and burnt alum.

Lit: Barrett & Thorpe, 1971, *op. cit.*, Pl.80.

Bradley, 1978, *op. cit.*, Advertisement at end with different style of decoration, and Pl.124 without pots and taper stick.

Twitchett, 1980, *op. cit.*, Pl.32 for similar shape.

Dawson, 1987, *op. cit.*, Pl.39, p.34 for similar shape.

Lippert, 1987, *op. cit.*, Cat. No.23, p.125 for larger size (25.1 cm.).

See: Victoria & Albert Museum (Schr. 1.321) for similar shape.

Lit: Hobson, 1905, *op. cit.*, Cat.Porc.II 46 and II 47 for similar shape, but smaller cut-out hole in the unglazed top, both examples decorated with floral sprays and the moulded decoration white. Three very large firing cracks in the base of one, and burst bubbles in the paste, leaving unglazed marks on the inside surface.

Stoner, 1955, *op. cit.*, Pl.102, for Bow example.

Gabszewicz & Freeman, 1982, *op. cit.*, Pl.179 for Bow example marked with an anchor and dagger.

22. PEDESTAL STAND

*c.*1760

Of rectangular shape with *bombé* front and flat unglazed back, with moulded rococo scroll supports at the four corners and a moulded shell scroll in the centre on the base. A flat unglazed top, with a large circular hole cut in the centre and a shallow groove near the outside edge.

Painted, in a rectangular reserve in the centre, with a rural landscape in naturalistic enamel colours, with scattered insects on the side panels and the rococo scroll-moulded decoration picked out in turquoise enamel.

Mark: Patch marks.

H. 10 cm. L. 19.5 cm.   Derby Museum & Art Gallery (1621)

Prov: W.H. Moss Collection.

Lit: Scott, 1961, *Antique Porcelain Digest,* Bath. Pl.166, No.594 for Liverpool porcelain at Colonial Williamsburg, Williamsburg, Va.

Towner, 1963, *William Greatbach and the Early Wedgwood Wares,* Trans. E.C.C., Vol.5, Pt.4, Pls.180 & 181 for salt-glazed examples.

E.C.C., 1963, *Miscellany.* Trans. E.C.C., Vol.5, Pt.4, Pl.183 for creamware tortoiseshell with a transfer-print.

Barrett & Thorpe, 1971, *op. cit.,* Pl.78.

Williams, 1973, *op. cit.,* colour Pl.61.

Watney, 2nd Ed. 1973, *English Blue & White Porcelain of the 18th Century,* London. Pl.15b for Bow, & Pl.77b for Lowestoft examples.

Smith, 1975, *Lowestoft Porcelain in Norwich Castle Museum,* Gt. Yarmouth, Vol.1, Pl.680 & pp.59 & 115 for Lowestoft example.

Walton, 1976, *Creamware and other English Pottery at Temple Newsam House, Leeds,* London & Bradford, Pl.274 for deep creamware example.

Gabszewicz & Freeman, 1982, *op. cit.,* for Bow example.

Exhibition, 1983, Victoria & Albert Museum, *op. cit.,* Pl.O21 for Bow, and Pls. P10 & P11 for perhaps Wedgwood examples.

Hillis, 1985, *The Liverpool Porcelains,* N.C.S., Occasional Paper *No.1* Pl.67 for Brownlow Hill, Liverpool example.

Britton, 1987, *London Delftware,* Milton Keynes. Pl.141 for example of baluster-shape made in London.

23. WALL-POCKET (One of a pair)   *c.*1770

Of cornucopia shape with elaborately moulded rococo scrolls forming a reserve, with slightly everted rococo scroll rim and slightly depressed and inward-sloping shoulder with cut-out crescent and six circular holes, and a flat back with shaped dome top, pierced with two holes suitable for hanging purposes. The moulding on the foot spiralling towards the right end and, on the matching pair, to the left.

Painted in the reserves in polychrome enamel colours with exotic birds perched amongst foliage.

It is presumed that these wall-pockets were intended for flowers, probably dried flowers, in the manner shown in a print by J. June after C. Fenn (reproduced in the *Ladies Amusement,* 1966, Pl.18). But no contemporary picture or print is known showing such wall-pockets in a domestic setting. They were made in salt-glazed stoneware, tin-glazed earthenware, creamware and porcelain, from about 1740-1770; also in Chinese Export ware *c.*1780, which were made to 'slot on' to a wall pinhead.

Mark: Patch marks.

L. 24.3 cm.   Derby Museum & Art Gallery (165-1984)

Figures in the
Early 'Patch Mark' Period
1756-1765

The change in the management in the Derby China Factory following the arrival of William Duesbury in 1756, also resulted in a change in the design and decoration of the figures produced there. Based on his experience gained whilst working as a decorator in London, Duesbury was fully conversant with the fashionable demands of his clients so that when he took over the management of the factory, it followed that he would try to produce wares that would meet the fashion-conscious metropolitan demands. This meant copying figures first produced at Meissen, and it was Duesbury's boast that they were 'after the finest Dresden models'; 'the nearest to Dresden'; 'that many good judges could not distinguish them from the real Dresden'; and going so far as to call the wares 'Derby Porcelain or second Dresden'.

The figures made during Duesbury's early years as manager indicate a change and were produced using a lighter paste with an improved glaze. This paste was more easily governed and the figures have been described as 'the pale family', due to the pale colourings. They also give the impression of having undergone a blue 'rinse'. The colours chiefly employed in the decoration include yellow, a dull turquoise, and a pinkish crimson (Fig.24 is decorated in this manner.)

It was still the custom to place small figures on the dining table (Fig.25) and some of the earlier pairs of figures were adapted to shell baskets in which sweetmeats could be placed (Fig.26). It would seem that when short of new ideas, the modellers sought inspiration from some of the earlier Meissen models and the boy holding a posy (Fig.27), which was paired with a girl companion holding a basket of fruit, was copied from an earlier example modelled by J.F. Eberlein.

One very rare figure from this period,[1] is a candlestick figure of 'Spring as a Cherub', with the candle holder modelled as a tree trunk at the back. Although the figure is quite commonplace, what makes it so interesting is the incised date, just discernible as 1760[2] followed by '1Marl. 1 Flint. Waite [water?]. White Clay', indicating possibly a change in the composition of the clay body — the body being quite hard and very white with a very high glaze — and therefore an experimental reference piece.

The rococo style was still popular during the 1760s, and the figures then being produced reflected this demand, with a plethora of 'S' or 'C' scroll ornamentation. In the candlestick based on one of *Aesop's Fables* (Fig.28), the bocage is used to create a natural setting, whereas the figure playing the mandolin (Fig.29) is rather overshadowed by the surrounding background.

Duesbury's chief rival at this period was Chelsea, and as if to prove that the wares produced at Derby were equal to anything produced in London, a deliberate attempt was made to copy Chelsea and these two candlesticks show what could be done. Ideas were also borrowed from the *Commedia dell'Arte* series (Fig.30), which had been produced at Meissen in 1745 and first produced at Derby in 1758. Evidently the group must have been popular for it was still being produced over ten years later in a later, adapted, style which was designed to be more in keeping with the fashion which was then in vogue.

'Patch marks' have been recorded on some Chelsea pieces and it was not until it was realised that figures produced after 1770 which also have an incised model number under the base, and that these numbers correspond with numbers on a Derby descriptive price list, that Derby products were correctly identified as such. Before this elucidation, in 1925, much of the Derby made before 1770, was attributed to either Chelsea or Bow and, even now, there are still examples of early Derby which are wrongly classified.

1.   International Ceramics Fair, June, 1989, held at The Park Lane Hotel, London.
2.   G. Godden *Encyclopaedia of British Porcelain Manufacturers* p.294, Pl.140 where the incised date is given as 1762 or 1768.

Lit: Barrett & Thorpe, 1971, *op. cit.,* Pl.25 for boy wearing different coloured clothes, and replacement left hand, not holding an egg.

Lippert, 1987, *op.cit.* Cat.No.21, p.121, wearing flowered costume, and smaller size (18.7 cm.).

24. CHINESE BOY ROBBING A BIRD'S NEST   *c.*1758-60

Figure of a shaven-headed Chinese boy climbing a tree and partially entwined in its tendril branches with his right leg sticking through the tendrils, and his right arm raised grasping a branch, whilst holding a bird's egg in his left hand.

The figure painted in naturalistic enamel colours, his open-necked garment puce, lined with green, and yellow boots, and the tendril branches of the tree painted with green, yellow and red markings.

Mark: Four patch marks.

H. 24 cm.   Derby Museum & Art Gallery (559-1979)

25. FIFE AND DRUM PLAYER   *c.1756-60*

Figure of a small boy dressed in a jacket, waistcoat, knee-breeches, buckle shoes and wearing a hat with an up-turned brim, with his right leg bent slightly, supported by a stump, holding, in his left hand a fife and with a small drum suspended from his neck, which he is in the act of striking with his right hand. Set on a shell-mound base.

Painted in enamel colours with the jacket pale puce. The waistcoat and breeches decorated with floral motifs.

Mark: Patch marks

H. 13.5 cm.   Derby Museum & Art Gallery (372-58)

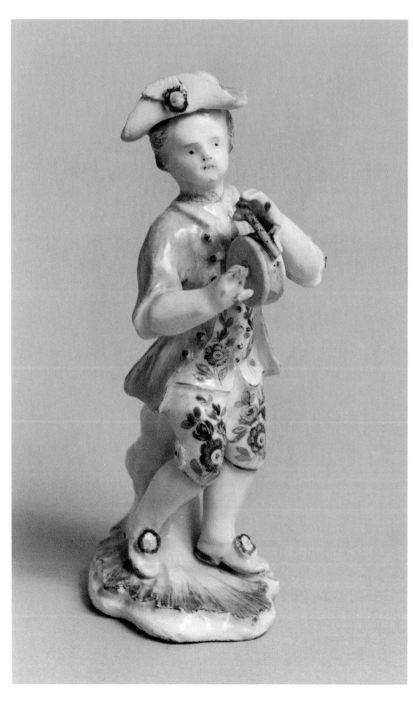

Lit: Barrett & Thorpe, 1971, *op. cit.,* Pl.49, p.18.

Twitchett, 1980, *op. cit.,* Pl.45 for slightly different model.

26. NEGRO BOY

Figure of a negro boy wearing a garment with high frilly neck, elbow-length loose sleeves, yellow breeches and white stockings, kneeling on his right knee and holding in his hands a large shell-shaped dish, supported on his bent left knee, set on a rocaille base.

Painted in naturalistic enamel colours with his face and arms dark brown, turquoise jacket edged with gilt, white sleeves, yellow breeches, white stockings and black shoes, with gold stud earrings in his ears. The base painted turquoise and green and the scroll moulding picked out in gold.

There is a companion figure of a negress in a similar posture.

Mark: Patch marks.

H. 20 cm.   Derby Museum & Art Gallery (530-61)

See: Victoria & Albert Museum (Schr. 1.302) for similar example.

27.   BOY HOLDING A POSY   *c.1765-70*

Model of a boy wearing a cut-away coat, waistcoat, cummerbund, breeches, stockings and buckle shoes, with long hair held in place with a ribbon hanging down his back, holding an up-turned hat filled with flowers in his right hand (broken off and incorrect hand replacement), and a posy in his left hand. Set on a low mound base with scattered moulded leaves.

Copied from an earlier version modelled at Meissen by J.F. Eberlein.

Paired with a girl companion, standing holding a basket of fruit in one hand and an apple in the other.

Painted in enamel colours, with the lining of the coat turquoise, the cummerbund pink and the breeches pale yellow.

Mark: Patch marks and incised 'N'.

H. 16 cm.   Derby Museum & Art Gallery (564)

See: Carlisle Museum & Art Gallery (9-1940-150ii) for similar example.

Lit: Gilhespy, 1951, *op. cit.,* fig.145, formerly in the Victoria & Albert Museum, Circulation Department.

Barrett & Thorpe, 1971, *op. cit.,* Pl.58 for earlier version with two dogs barking at a squirrel in a tree.

Rice, 1983, *op. cit.,* Pl.75a.

Adams, 1987, *op. cit.,* for Chelsea example.

Lippert, 1987, *op. cit.,* Cat.No.10, p.85 for two Chelsea examples.

28. FABLE CANDLESTICK   *c.*1765

A candlestick modelled as a tree trunk, with one of the branches at the back forming a loop handle, making it suitable for carrying, and surmounted by a candle nozzle in the shape of a flower rising from a spread of moulded leaves. The tree covered with bocage, in which two birds are nesting, and on a low apron scroll mound in front a spaniel-type dog is barking, looking up at the birds.

Painted in naturalistic enamel colours.

This idea would seem to have been adapted from one of *Aesop's Fables,* with other examples including a squirrel in a tree and the selfish ass hiding in a tree all being worried by dogs.

Mark: Patch marks.

H. 21 cm.   Derby Museum & Art Gallery (532-1910

29. FIGURE IN GAZEBO CANDLESTICK *c.1765*

A lady wearing a dark bodice, long skirt and a hat, turned slightly to the right, playing a mandolin, seated beneath an elaborate trellis structure adorned with applied floral sprays in relief and flanked by branches supporting pierced candle nozzles (branches and candle nozzles broken off) and surmounted by an hexagonal dovecot with pagoda-like top and onion finial. The raised base, which is decorated with applied flowers, rests on four scroll feet above which there is a pierced apron surmounted by a trellis.

Derived from a Meissen model, with bagpipe player. Similar style figures, with candle brackets were made at Chelsea, marked Gold Anchor (1758-69).

Painted in naturalistic enamel colours.

Mark: Patch marks.

36.8 cm.   Derby Museum & Art Gallery (693-2-65)

Lit: F. Stoner, 1924, *Chelsea Moulds: an Important Discovery, Connoisseur* Vol. LXIX No.273, May.Pl.No.III for ill. of mould of companion bagpipe player.

Honey, Rackham and Read, 1926, *Early Derby Porcelain. Burlington Magazine,* Vol.XLIX, no.cclxxv, December. Pls.I and IIa and p.296.

Honey, 1928, *Old English Porcelain,* London. pps.107 and 262.

King, 1938, *The Wallace Elliot Bequest of English Porcelain and Pottery, British Museum Quarterly,* Vol.XII, no.3, p.77.

Lane, 1961, *op. cit.,* London. p.103.

Savage, 1961, *English Pottery and Porcelain,* London. Pl.140.

Barrett & Thorpe, 1971, *op. cit.,* Pl.72, p.23.

30. ISABELLA, GALLANT AND JESTER

c.1765-70

A pastoral group consisting of two lovers seated side by side lost in rapture. The girl wearing a bodice laced in the front and a skirt over a petticoat and shoes and a small head-dress, sitting with a small dog in her lap, glancing up at the youth who is wearing a jacket over a waistcoat, knee breeches, stockings and shoes, with his left hand gesturing towards his heart and his right arm round the girl's shoulders. They are interrupted in their reverie by a clown, wearing a short jerkin, knee breeches, stockings and shoes, offering them a small repast on a tray (missing). The group is surrounded by bocage and set on a rococo scroll mound. It was first produced at Derby in *c*.1758.

Taken from the *Commedia dell'Arte* series, this was originally adapted from a Meissen group, modelled by Johann Joachim Kändler, and first produced in 1745.

Painted in naturalistic enamel colours and gilt.

Mark: Patch marks.

H. 27.5 cm.   Derby Museum & Art Gallery (908-1980)

See: Victoria & Albert Museum (Schr.1.290) for early version.

Royal Crown Derby Porcelain Company Museum for 1765 version with flowering tree stump.

Lit: Hackenbroch, 1957, *op. cit.,* Pl.272 for example of early and Pl.277 for later version.

Gilhespy, 1961, *op. cit.,* Pl.21 for early version without bocage.

Barrett & Thorpe, 1971, *op. cit.,* Pl.57, p.23.

Williams, 1973, *op. cit.,* Pl.15 for earlier *c*.1755, Group without bocage.

Twitchett, 1980, *op. cit.,* Pl.30, and col.Pl.13.

Rice, 1983, *op. cit.,* Pl.62 for early, and Pl.63 for later version wearing slightly different pattern clothing.

Later 'Patch Mark' Figures 1765–1800

The earlier rococo figures continued to be produced, but at the same time others of a more robust nature began to take over and the subjects chosen reflected the interests of the day including political and historical personages (Fig.31), as well as the arts and sciences. Although many of the figures continued to be based on earlier models, they had to be adapted to meet the neo-classical fashion and so instead of being set on elaborate rococo bases, they were now set on a simple rectangular-shaped base. The Four Seasons were adapted and produced in different sizes (Fig.32).

It was a time of great travel and world exploration and although Australasia was not then on the map, the Four Continents, or Four Quarters of the Globe as they were called, were a popular subject, with each continent represented by an animal, which it was thought typified the region, and a male or female figure dressed in accordance with tradition (Figs.33 & 34). Other figures included the Elements (Fig.35) and also those adapted from Greek and Roman mythology (Figs.36, 37 & 38).

Throughout this period Putti or Cherubs (Fig.39) were produced in great numbers and from the Lygo correspondence[1] we learn that large orders were placed by Mr Williams for export to France and Holland. Since 1770 when the ailing Chelsea porcelain factory had been purchased by Duesbury, he was almost without a rival in the production of porcelain figures. It was in that year that the London showrooms were opened. The wares on display included both Derby and Chelsea — run until 1784 in conjunction with Derby — and the trade card which was issued advertising the Chelsea wares also included 'Derbyshire Fluors, Alabasters, Marbles etc.', which could be seen and admired by 'Royalty, Nobility, Gentry etc., and Public in General', with a special note to say that 'The Rooms are well air'd'.

Leading artists of the day, living both at home and abroad, were commissioned to produce works and, to ensure that their work would be done exclusively for Duesbury, some were asked to sign agreements.

Very rarely are the models ever signed, however, and it is therefore difficult to attribute them definitely to any particular artist. In the Account Book, referred to on page 14, mention is made of a payment in December 1773, to Mr Cunningham for a model of 'Macaley' (sic), and other artists' names mentioned in the Lygo correspondence include Henry Webber (1754-1826), the son of a Swiss sculptor; Charles Horwell (b.1754); John Deare (1759-98), all of whom attended the Royal Academy Schools in 1777. There is also an almost indecipherable entry in the Duesbury Account Book 'for employing the Deares', though at that date, 1774, John Deare would have been too young for the entry to refer to him.

Keen competition must have existed between William Duesbury and Josiah Wedgwood in trying to attract the best modellers, and in January 1785, Henry Webber, who had been a pupil of John Bacon, signed a seven year agreement with Wedgwood. Two years later he was sent to Rome 'for the purpose of making models, drawings and other improvements in the art of modelling and designing for the benefit of the said Josiah Wedgwood'.[2] Charles Peart (1759-98), who also did work for Wedgwood after leaving the Royal Academy Schools in 1781, is mentioned by Lygo; and his school contemporary John Charles Felix Rossi (1762-1839) worked at the Derby China Works in 1788, before moving in the following year to work for Vulliamy, the King's clock maker, who was an important customer.

Lygo also mentioned the name of B.F. Hardenberg, who in 1800 exhibited at the Royal Academy *The Four Seasons decorating an Urn*; and William John Coffee, who became a modeller at the Derby China Factory in 1792, before moving to the newly opened Pinxton China Factory in 1793, where he remained for ten years, before emigrating to America.

Writing in 1876, John Haslem[3] compiled a list of Derby groups and single figures, both enamelled and gilt, and in biscuit, and against each item was marked the size, height, and price of both the decorated and the biscuit version. However, since no date is given, it is not clear to what prices they refer.[4] So, when the list was reprinted by Barrett & Thorpe,[5] the price figures were omitted. However what is of supreme importance is that the list establishes what had been made at the Derby Factory.

1. Lygo correspondence p.12 February, 1789.
2. Gunnis, 1953, *Dictionary of British Sculptors 1660-1851* p.417.
3. Haslem, 1876 (reprint 1973), *The Old Derby China Factory* pps.170-181.
4. For the different list published by Bemrose see Lane *op. cit.*
5. Barrett & Thorpe, 1971, *op. cit.* pps.180-192.

31. SHAKESPEARE

Figure standing with his legs elegantly crossed, leaning with his right elbow on a pile of books, placed on a tall pedestal, set on a base raised on four scroll feet, which is adorned with the heads of Henry V, Richard III and Elizabeth I. The index finger of his left hand pointing to a scroll, fallen open to reveal the quotation beginning 'The cloud capt Towers' from *The Tempest*. Painted in naturalistic enamel colours with the lining of the robe painted in puce enamel.

Model based on the Scheemakers figure, designed by William Kent, and erected in Poet's Corner, Westminster Abbey, in 1741.

Derby also produced companion figure of Milton.

Mark: Patch marks

H. 28.5 cm.   Derby Museum & Art Gallery (291)

See: Victoria & Albert Museum (C.91-1870) for coloured example also (C.260-1976) for example in 'biscuit'.

Lit: Jewitt, 1878, *The Ceramic Art of Great Britain*, London. pp.68-9, stating that one was included in the list of items which were sent to London in 1763.

King, 1925, *English Porcelain Figures of the Eighteenth Century*, London. Fig.41.

Williams, 1973, *op. cit.,* Pl.55.

Twitchett, 1980, *op. cit.,* Pl.83 for similar example and Pl.67 for earlier version.

Rice, 1983, *op. cit.,* pp.48 & 188.

Lippert, 1987, *op. cit.,* Cat.No.25, p.131, with the quotation, except for SHALL DISSOLVE, written out in longhand.

See: Victoria & Albert Museum (Schr.1.341) for figure set on a rococo scroll base, with additional moulded vines round the body of Bacchus.

Lit: Haslem, 1876 (reprint 1973), *op. cit.*, lists: 'Set of Four Chelsea Standing Seasons, in 3 sizes'.

Gilhespy, 1951, *op. cit.*, fig.150 for Meissen original.

Gilhespy, 1965, *op. cit.*, Pl.20 for full set.

Barrett & Thorpe, 1971, *op. cit.*, Pl.50.

Twitchett, 1980, *op. cit.*, Pl.56 for earlier example.

Bradshaw, 1981, *op. cit.*, Pl.114 for earlier version on rococo scroll base, *c*.1758.

32.   BACCHUS WITH YOUTHFUL SATYR   *c.*1770

Figure of Bacchus standing by a tree stump from which springs a vine with bunches of grapes and foliage, which are twined discreetly around his waist, his right arm is resting on the tree stump and with his left hand he holds a bunch of grapes above his mouth. Behind him, a youthful satyr is seated on a barrel holding a drinking goblet. Set on a flat rectangular base.

Painted in naturalistic enamel colours. One of the set 'The Seasons' representing 'Autumn'.

'The Seasons' were copied originally from a Meissen set, modelled probably by Johann Friedrich Eberlein.

Mark: Patch Marks

H. 22cm.   Derby Museum & Art Gallery

33. ASIA *c.*1770-75

A young Levantine girl with bare shoulders and wearing loose-fitting drapery, a wreath of apples on her head, holding a bunch of grapes in her left hand and a flaming vase (missing) in her right, standing in front of a camel crouching on the ground looking up towards her. Set on a pierced rocaille base covered with applied flowers and foliage and inscribed 'ASIA'. Painted in naturalistic enamel colours and gilt.

One of the set 'The Four Quarters of the Globe', copied from the second set modelled by Friedrich Elias Meyer at Meissen.

Companion piece to 'America'. (See Fig.34) Also copied at Chelsea *c.*1759.

Mark: Patch marks

H. 22.5 cm.   Derby Museum & Art Gallery (288-1)

See: Victoria & Albert Museum (Schr.1.184) for earlier example.

Lit: Lane, 1961, *op. cit.,* Pls.22b & 23a.

Gilhespy, 1965, *op. cit.,* Pl.149 for set with slightly different decoration (formerly in Hurlbutt Collection).

Morley-Fletcher, 1968, *Investing in Pottery and Porcelain,* London. p.137.

Spero, 1970, *op. cit.,* p.411 for similar example.

Twitchett, 1980, *op. cit.,* Pl.104 for earlier example.

Bradshaw, 1981, *op. cit.,* Pl.113 for much later copy.

Rice, 1983, *op. cit.,* Pl.87, p.194, for earlier model.

34. AMERICA *c*.1770-75

A young Red Indian boy wearing a loincloth of feathers, with feathers in his hair, a quiver of arrows slung over his shoulder, holding a bow in his right hand and an arrow (broken off) in the other, resting against a tree trunk, with his right foot treading on an alligator with open mouth. Set on a pierced rocaille base covered with applied flowers and foliage and inscribed 'AMERICA'. Companion to 'Asia'. See Fig. 33.

Painted in naturalistic enamel colours.

Mark: Patch marks. Incised No. 200.

H. 24.5 cm. Derby Museum & Art Gallery (1512)

35. NEPTUNE
*c.*1770

Figure of the sea god Neptune, standing in a threatening attitude, with a flowing beard and naked except for a flowered cloak, billowing out over his left shoulder and around his waist, with a crown on his head and holding, in his left hand, a gilt-metal trident, standing beside a dolphin issuing a torrent of water from its mouth, both set on a high shell-encrusted rock, with a rococo scroll base, decorated with moulded shells and seaweed.

The figure painted in naturalistic enamel colours and the dolphin in green, the cloak painted with a floral design on the outside and lined in dark pink, the shells and seaweed picked out in naturalistic enamel colours, with sparse gilding.

Neptune formed part of the set of The Four Elements.

Mark: Patch marks and incised script 'No.92/2 and TUT' and incised 'star'.

H. 21 cm.   Derby Museum & Art Gallery (714-1965)

See: British Museum (Reg. No.1940, 11-1, 28) Miss F. Laura Cannan Bequest, set on a different base, without scrolls.

Victoria & Albert Museum (Schr. 1.305) and Cecil Higgins Museum, Bedford, for slightly different version, marked with a Gold Anchor.

Lit: Haslem, 1876 (reprint 1973), *op. cit.* p.150, states that the ornamental repairer Isaac Farnsworth, used a sort of 'star' (four intersected lines) as his mark.

Rackham, 1928 revised, *Catalogue of the Schreiber Collection of English Porcelain,* London. Pl.35.

Gilhespy, 1951, *op. cit.,* Pl.2 for earlier version.

Scott, 1961, *op. cit.,* Bath. Pl.155, fig.530.

Barrett & Thorpe, 1971, *op. cit.,* Pl.96, p.43.

Watney, 1980, *Some Parallels and Prototypes in Ceramics,* Trans. E.C.C., Vol.10, Pt.5, Pls. 148a & b, for 'dry-edge' version *c.*1752.

Rowan, 1988, *op. cit.,* p.57 for 'biscuit' model figure of Neptune and model of the dolphin, made of saltglazed stoneware.

36. JUPITER AND THE EAGLE   *c.*1775

Figure of the god Jupiter, barefoot, in threatening mood, wearing a long flowered robe and loose cloak held over his right shoulder; with a crown on his head and brandishing a thunderbolt, held above his head in his right hand, with another in his left hand, hanging down at his side, standing beside an eagle, with its wings partially raised ready for flight, both set on a flat rectangular plinth.

The bearded figure and the eagle painted in naturalistic enamel colours, with Jupiter's floral garment, trimmed with blue, and his pink cloak tied with a yellow sash, and a brown line painted round all four sides of the plinth.

Companion to Juno (see Fig.37).

Mark: Incised No.117.

H. 18.5 cm.   Derby Museum & Art Gallery (1526)

See: Victoria & Albert Museum (C.309-1951) for earlier version.

Royal Crown Derby Museum, for earlier version.

Lit: King, 1925, *op. cit.* Fig.46.

Gilhespy, 1951, *op. cit.,* fig.175.

Barrett & Thorpe, 1971, *op. cit.,* Pl.91, p.42.

Twitchett, 1980, *op. cit.,* Col.Pl.7, for earlier version.

Rice, 1983, *op. cit.,* p.191.

37. JUNO   *c.*1775

Figure of the goddess Juno, wearing a loose veil and a cloak over her dress and sandals on her feet, with a crown on her head, holding a bowl in her left hand, and with her right stroking the head of the peacock, whose tail feathers are raised in display, standing beside her, on a flat square plinth.

The figure and the peacock painted in naturalistic enamel colours, with sunburst flower heads set in white reserves on an orange dress, trimmed with green, and a yellow veil held in place on her head by the crown and hanging down her back, with a brown line painted round the plinth.

Companion figure to Jupiter (Fig.36).

Mark: No. 119 and incised 'triangle'.

H. 16.3 cm.   Derby Museum & Art Gallery (352)

Lit: Haslem, 1876 (reprint 1973), *op. cit.,* p.150, states that the repairer Joseph Hill used an incised 'triangle', as his mark.

King, 1925, *op. cit.,* fig.45.

Gilhespy, 1951, *op. cit.,* fig.176.

Barrett & Thorpe, 1971, *op. cit.,* as Fig. 36.

Twitchett, 1980, *op. cit.,* as Fig. 36.

38. JASON AND MEDEA BEFORE ARTEMIS *c.*1773

Jason dressed as a Greek warrior wearing military tunic, sandals and helmet surmounted by a plume, half kneeling on his left knee with the other leg bent, touching his breast with the fingers of his right hand and his left arm raised above his head, gazing up at Medea, who stands holding her cloak with her left hand and, with the elbow of her right arm resting on the plinth, points upwards. Both are making a vow to Artemis, the goddess of hunting, who stands on a raised plinth towering above them, touching her bosom with the fingers of her left hand and the other arm hanging loosely at her side. Jason's shield rests propped against the base of the plinth which is decorated with the head of a deer, and the low mound is embellished with scattered flowers.

Painted in naturalistic enamel colours and gilt.

Mark: Incised No.37, and 2 (for second size).

H. 32 cm. Derby Museum & Art Gallery (387–1979)

Lit: J.E. Nightingale, 1881, *Contributions towards the History of Early English Porcelain from Contemporary Sources,* Salisbury. Sale Catalogue 9–10 February 1773 p.41.

Barrett & Thorpe, 1971, *op. cit.,* p.164.

Twitchett, 1980, *op. cit.,* Pl.103.

39. PUTTI   *c.*1785

Three figures of putti, in different sizes, each carrying a basket of flowers and bedecked with floral garlands, supported by a floral stump, and each set on a mound base.

Painted in naturalistic enamel colours.

Mark: Patch marks. One incised with (?)'5'. Another incised 'OE5' and 'Star'.

H. 10.5 cm., H. 11 cm., H. 14.5 cm., respectively.

Derby Museum & Art Gallery (351 for tallest and 385 for other two)

See: Fig.35, for reference to incised 'Star' mark.

Lit: Barrett & Thorpe, 1971, *op. cit.,* Pl.88, p.42.

Twitchett, 1980, *op. cit.,* Pl.86 for early *c.*1756-8 version.

Gabszewicz & Freeman, 1982, *op. cit.,* Pl.236 for example made at Bow.

Unglazed Porcelain Figures

The fashion for unglazed porcelain figures may well have started as a reaction against more highly decorated wares; but from the time when they were first introduced at Sèvres they have always attracted a keen interest amongst discerning collectors. The fact that they were more expensive to produce than coloured examples may have given them a certain 'snob' attraction, and also, because the finished result had to be as near perfect as possible, they were more closely scrutinized before being allowed to leave the factory.

From the early days of porcelain production the ceramic artist/decorators disguised any flaws, such as a bubble or tear in the paste, by painting insects or flowers over the blemish. The thickness of the glaze also helped to hide other faults in the 'repairer's' work, but this was not possible when the item was left as 'biscuit'.

It is thought that the Vincennes–Sèvres factory was the first to produce and market unglazed porcelain figures, where they were seen and admired by Madame de Pompadour, who started to collect them. Interest in them spread rapidly and to satisfy the demands of other European courts and aristocratic houses, ceramic factories in other parts of Europe were soon producing unglazed biscuit figures.

Naturally it was not long before the fashion spread to England and in the Royal Collection are three Derby biscuit groups[1] which have been attributed to John Bacon (1740-99). The models are based on a picture painted by Zoffany (1733-1810) in 1770, and engraved by R. Earlom (1743-1822), depicting George III in 'Van Dyck' costume, standing resting his left arm on a pillar which is surmounted by the crown resting on a cushion; Queen Charlotte sitting nursing Princess Augusta with Princess Charlotte (later created Princess Royal) standing beside her mother; and in the third group, the four young Princes, George, Prince of Wales (later George IV) and Fredrick (later Duke of York, but known then as the Bishop of Osnaburgh) standing, with William (later William IV) seated and Edward (later Duke of Kent and the father of Queen Victoria) in long clothes, sitting on the floor. Princess Elizabeth, who would have been born after this painting by Zoffany was completed, was not included in the family group, and neither she nor Prince Ernest Augustus were added, though both were born before 1772, when this model was made. This triple group was last seen in public at the Burlington House Fair in 1985, when they were graciously loaned to the Exhibition by Her Majesty The Queen and formed part of the display of Derby porcelain assembled by the exhibition organising committee of the Derby Porcelain International Society.

It is interesting to note that in the Christie & Ansell auction sale held on Tuesday 5 May, 1778, a coloured version of George III was sold for £3 10s. Another, bearing the Chelsea/Derby mark, was sold in 1875 for £47, though in the footnote on p.62 [2] it is stated that the infant Princess is Sophia, who was not born until 1778.

As stated, the modelling of this group is attributed to John Bacon of whom Henry Duesbury wrote from London to John Haslem on 27 November 1862 'I see by an old mem. book now before me (of my great grandfather) that he paid Bacon, the first sculptor of the day £74 7s 2d in 1769 for models; this is a point worth noting, as showing his determination to have the best that could be got.'[3] Unfortunately he gives no details of this purchase, nor does he state when the bill was incurred. It is known that at the age of fourteen, Bacon was apprenticed to Nicholas Crisp on 6 June 1755,[4] and that in 1768 he entered the Royal Academy Schools; about 1769 he became a modeller working for Mrs Coade (of Coade's Artificial Stone) and that earlier that year he was employed by Wedgwood, who opened his Ornamental Works at Etruria in 1769. Also in that same year he won the first Gold Medal for sculpture awarded by the Academy[5] and one is left wondering whether the date given by Duesbury is correct. The date is also repeated by Barrett & Thorpe adding that this is the only known authentic information linking this artist with the Derby factory.

Many of the model makers employed by Duesbury were of French extraction, working at Tournai before coming to England. Nicholas Joseph François Gauron was on the payroll at Chelsea, where he was paid 8s 9d per day and his duties were specified as being those of a figure maker. Partly due to the absence of other known names, it was thought that most of the more elaborate models at Chelsea were made by him and that the maquettes and moulds were sent from London to Derby. It was once thought that Gauron brought with him his original moulds, but since these moulds were not made use of at the other factories on the continent where he worked before coming to England, this supposition has now been abandoned.

In her lecture given at The International Ceramics Fair in June 1988,[6] Mireille Jottrand drew attention to the fine work done by Pierre Stephan before he left Tournai and quoted a bill dated 1769, which mentions his name in relation to a set of The Elements. This was the year before he signed an agreement with William Duesbury to work as a modeller and china or porcelain 'repairer'. The agreement was dated 17 September 1770 and was to last for three years. This was after Duesbury had taken control of the Chelsea factory, but Stephan must have worked at Derby, because when he wrote to Wedgwood he stated in his letter dated 9 May, 1774, that he had worked at Derby and later at the newly opened factory at Wirksworth. Evidently his application for work was accepted, since he moved to Wedgwood, but in another letter dated Etruria, 22 August 1774, Josiah Wedgwood writing to Bentley criticises his work. Whether he then worked as a freelance modeller is uncertain, but it is stated that he continued to supply models to Derby even as late as 1795.[7]

A sale catalogue, reprinted in full by J.E. Nightingale,[8] lists the items which were sold by Mr Christie during a four day auction sale held in London, starting on Wednesday 17 April, 1771. In the announcement it is stated that it is the first public sale of the 'Chelsea and Derby Porcelaine (sic) Manufactories'; and that the items to be sold were 'Last Year's Produce' and is the first time that items 'in biscuit' are mentioned. Though they were split up during the four day sale they included:-

'A fine group of the Virtues, with Minerva crowning Constancy with a garland of flowers, and Hercules killing the Hydra, in biscuit' (15 lots)

'Two pair Bacchus and Cupid, riding on a goat and panther, with oblong pedestals, emboss'd festoons, in biscuit' (8 lots)

'A set of curious antique season vases, on pedestals, in biscuit' (10 lots)

'Pair of antique vases, in biscuit', also 'on pedestals, for a desert' (5 lots)

'Four antique urns and pedestals, in biscuit' (1 lot)

'A very curious pair of figures, Prudence and Discression, each with antique urns on a pedestal, in biscuit' (5 lots)

'Two curious figures, with an alter-piece, in biscuit' (5 lots)

'A pair of fine figures, Gardener and Companion, in biscuit' (4 lots)

'A pair of curious figures sitting, most elegantly finish'd with lace, in biscuit' (4 lots)

'A pair of sitting figures, a gentleman reading, and a lady knotting, most curiously ornamented with lace, in biscuit' (7 lots)

'A pair of elegant sitting figures, a gentleman reading, and a lady playing on musick, most curiously finish'd with lace, in biscuit' (1 lot)

'A gentleman playing on the flute, and a lady singing, most curiously finished, with lace, in biscuit' (3 lots)

In the introduction to another two-day sale held on Tuesday the 9 and Wednesday the 10 of February, 1773, of the previous year's production of the Derby and Chelsea Porcelaine Manufactories, it is stated 'The Biscuit Groups and Figures, of which there are great Variety, are modelled with the utmost Nicety, and particularly suited for the Embellishment of Deserts'. Amongst the lots to be sold are 'Two groups of the elements Earth and Air, finely modelled in biscuit'; also Fire and Water, and amongst the mythological figures and muses: Euterpe, Polyhymnia, Thalia, Urania, Erato, Melpomene, Clio, Calliope and Terpsichore, as well as Apollo — indicative perhaps, of the classical knowledge of educated customers in the eighteenth century. Groups of the Arts and Sciences (painting, sculpture, music and astronomy, also poetry and grammar), all in biscuit, were also sold. And in later sales there were busts of Garrick, Voltaire, Shakespeare, Horace, Chaucer and Mrs Macaulay, the historian, in biscuit, sometimes set on an enamelled pedestal. These busts would presumably have been placed on top of a bookcase in a gentleman's library, rather in the manner of the Wedgwood basalt busts.

One lot is described simply as 'One figure of Christ' and another 'One pair of figures, Madonna and prudent mother, in biscuit', possibly produced for the export market. Also 'One group of a galantee-show, and one ditto, playing at hazard, in biscuit'. Certainly 'Neptune and Amphitrite drawn by 3 sea horses, in biscuit', must have looked magnificent. In a sale in December 1783, one lot was listed as 'A bust of the Queen, and six figures, in biscuit', and another 'A tablet in biscuit', without giving any further information.

Clearly the range of wares produced during this period lived up to the auctioneer's description of 'great Variety', and the illustrated pieces shown here only represents a very small part of the factories production. Occasionally the pieces are marked, but more usually incised with a reference number and because they were produced in different sizes, the size number is often also incised as a reference to be used when ordering.

It should not be forgotten that Vulliamy, the famous clock maker, was an important customer and in the account book in the British Museum there is an entry 'Sold to Mr. Vulliamy on January 29, 1791':

2 Sitting female figures, bisc't £12.12.0.

1 Standing Angel   6. 6. 0.

3 Standing Boys   1.11.6.

and another entry dated 11 September, 1794:

'Rec'd of Mr. Vulliamy £100. 0. 0. cash'.

These figures and other groups were used to embellish his clocks and were based on commissions given to sculptors to model, the model then being passed on to Derby where it would be translated into porcelain. It has been stated[9] that Vulliamy thought Charles Peart 'the most capable'. John Charles Felix Rossi's (1762-1839) name has been suggested in connection with the order quoted above because he was working at Derby in 1788 and 1789,[10] after attending the Royal Academy School in 1781. But he would have left Derby by the time the above figures were made. However, it is possible that these could have been the work of Jean Jacques Spängler who had been introduced to Vulliamy by Joseph Lygo in May 1790, shortly after his arrival in England. Later that year Spängler signed an agreement with Duesbury to work at Derby, but within two years he had broken the agreement and returned to London, causing Duesbury II much trouble and embarrassment by being committed to prison. Nevertheless, a new agreement was signed in 1795 and Spängler returned to Derby, but it was not long before he disappeared again, this time never to return.[11]

In spite of the trouble he must have caused, the fact that Duesbury was prepared to sign a second agreement must indicate how highly his work was thought of.

1. Derby Porcelain International Society, Journal No.1, Ill. 18.
2. Nightingale, 1881 (reprint 1973), *op. cit.* p.62.
3. Haslem, 1876 (reprint 1973), *op. cit.* p.43.
4. Watney 1989, *The Vauxhall China Works 1751-1764* Trans. E.C.C. Vol.13, Pt 3, p.215.
5. Barrett & Thorpe, 1971, *op. cit.* p.75
6. Jottrand, 1989, *New Thoughts on Tournai Porcelain Sculpture, The International Ceramics Fair and Seminar* pps.29-34.
7. Clifford, 1969, *Derby Biscuit*, Trans. E.C.C., Vol.7, Pt.2, pps.108-117.
8. Nightingale, 1881 (reprint 1973), *op. cit.*, pps.15-92.
9. Barrett & Thorpe, 1971, *op. cit.*, p.4.
10. Lane, 1961, *op. cit.*, p.109.
11. Barrett & Thorpe, 1971 *op. cit.*, p.104.

40. PASTORAL GROUP OF TWO FIGURES *c.*1778

A pastoral group with a shepherdess seated on a rock looking down at a youth seated on a lower rock, who has taken her right hand in his as a token of affection, and is gazing up at her; a lamb is lying contentedly on the ground beside her. The lover is wearing a short-sleeved jacket over a waistcoat, breeches and a cravat and she wears a bodice laced in front and a voluminous skirt over a petticoat and shoes fastened with bows. Set on a low mound with scattered clumps of flowers, set in the rockwork.

Copied from the Sèvres group, known as *La Bergère des Alpes*, modelled in 1766, by Etienne M. Falconet, after a design by François Boucher.

Biscuit.

Mark: No. 178 incised.

H. 18 cm. w. 14.5 cm.   Derby Museum & Art Gallery (452)

See: Victoria & Albert Museum (Schr.1.420) for model in colour, set on a high mound, with bocage added.

Lit: Clifford, 1969, *op. cit.* Pl.123, p.113 for example on high mound, with bocage.

Twitchett, 1980, *op. cit.,* Col.Pl.16, in 'biscuit' and Pl.130 in colour, both with added bocage.

Bourgeois, 1909, Le Biscuit de Sèvres au Dix-huitieme siêcle, Paris.

41. CUPID WITH A FALCON   *c*.1775–80

Cupid, with wings, sitting on a raised mound rock, beside a tree stump watching a hooded falcon perched on his right wrist.

Biscuit.

Mark: No. 213 incised.

H. 15 cm.   Derby Museum & Art Gallery (414)

42.   CUPID WITH A DOG   *c.*1775–80

Cupid, again with wings, relaxing on a rock, leaning back against a tree stump, with his right hand stroking a dog sitting beside him, trying to lick his face, and holding the dog's forepaw in his left hand.

Biscuit.

Mark: No.213 incised.

H. 13 cm.   Derby Museum & Art Gallery (442)

43.   TWO BACCHANTES WORSHIPPING A HERM OF PAN

c.1778

Two bacchantes, standing on a high rock pedestal in front of a tree, against which is the herm of Pan. One of the bacchantes stands looking up at Pan, with her right arm raised and holding in her hand a bunch of flowers; the other figure is kneeling beside her, in the act of twining a garland of flowers around Pan, with an ewer, a tambourine and a thyrsus all lying on the ground which is scattered with clumps of flowers.

Biscuit.

Mark: Crown, crossed batons, six dots and 'D'. Incised No.196 and a 'star'. (See Fig.35, for reference to 'star' mark).

H. 32.9 cm.   Derby Museum & Art Gallery (1533)

See: Victoria & Albert Museum (C.307-1940) attributed to Stephan, also (C.193-1926) for coloured example, marked 'N.196' and 'G' incised.

Note: Rackham, 1923, *op. cit.,* p.36 states 'Modelled by J.J. Spängler, after a design by Angelica Kauffmann, engraved by F. Bartolozzi'. However, Clifford, 1969, *op. cit.,*p.114, states that it is taken from an engraving *olim truncus eram Ficulus inutile Lignum* by Williams Wynne Ryland, published in May 1776, after a painting by Angelica Kauffmann, then in the Collection of the Duke of Northumberland. And Barrett & Thorpe, 1971, *op. cit.,* list it under models which are generally accepted as from Stephan's hand.

Note: Offered 5 May 1778 – £1 5s.

Lit: Bemrose, 1898, *op. cit.,* pp.94 & 126 and note on No.115.

Rackham, 1923, *op. cit.,* No.116, p.36, and Pl.30.

Clifford, 1969, *op. cit.,* Pl.121d, p.114.

Barrett & Thorpe, 1971, *op. cit.,* p.40, Pl.98.

Twitchett, 1980, *op. cit.,* Pl.116 & P125 for group painted in enamel colours.

Bradshaw, 1981, *op. cit.,* p.304.

44.   THREE MUSES WITH AN URN   *c.*1790-95

A group of three muses, Poetry, Painting and Science, represented by three maidens dressed in loose-fitting classical drapery and wearing sandals, standing with their back to a column by an urn, with one of the muses holding a scroll on which is incised the quotation from *A Midsummer Night's Dream* Act V, Scene 1, 'The Poet's eye, in a Fine frenzy Rolling / Doth glance from Heaven to Earth, from Earth to Heaven'. Lying at their feet are an open book, a globe and scattered leaves, set on a low mound (other attributes of the Arts missing).

Taken from an engraving by Marc Antonio Raimondi after Raphael, for a funerary monument to Francis I. *c.*1518/19, and later adapted by Germain Pilon (*c.*1535-1590) for the Monument of the Heart of Henri II (1539) for the Church of the Celestines, Louvre, Paris.

Biscuit.

Mark: Patch marks, Incised No.380.

H. 32 cm. w. 18.5 cm.   Derby Museum & Art Gallery (629)

Lit: Clifford, 1969, *op. cit.,* Pl.128, p.115.

Ornamental Vases

It is probable that the idea, in England, of using ceramic ornaments to decorate a room was first adopted by Queen Mary II, when she and her husband, King William III, established themselves at Hampton Court Palace. The fashion was already well established in Holland, where the Queen had been living since her marriage in 1677 to the Stadtholder. Some of her ceramic treasures can still be seen at Hampton Court today. These, of course, were chiefly oriental but also include Dutch Delft wares.

The changing political climate and increasingly prosperous trade allowed many of the new rich, as well as the old aristocratic families to set about rebuilding or re-designing their houses according to current fashion. The library assumed greater importance as a room where works of art and objects of interest acquired on the Grand Tour could be displayed and examined. These were imitated by others who had not seen the original Greek, Etruscan and Roman examples and so would not be so insistent on historical accuracy so long as they gave the right effect.

This coincided with the rise of the English ceramic factories and both Duesbury and Wedgwood were eager to meet the new demand. Working closely with architects and decorators and his London agent, Lygo, Duesbury was able to fulfil their special orders. The chimneypiece was one of the focal points of a room and it was therefore necessary for any ornaments to be placed on it to enhance the general effect.

The *garniture de cheminée* often consisted of a central item which was balanced on either side by other pieces, thus forming a group of either three or possibly five. Fig.49 is considered to have been designed by John Bacon R.A. (who is also known to have designed several chimney pieces) and though the claret and turquoise colours may not be to contemporary taste they and the other colours of pea-green and flesh pink, would have been ordered to harmonise with the colour scheme of the room, just as the vases with vertical stripe decoration (Fig.50) would have matched the 1780s style of interior decoration.

Whether they should be called 'Vases' or 'Urns' is a debatable point. Architects usually referred to them as 'Urns' when designed with covers but without handles, and 'Vases' included vessels with a spout for pouring. The general public preferred to call them 'Vases'. Wedgwood called the boom 'Vase madness' and in the London showrooms 'Vases' was all the cry. Certainly the Derby paste was more suitable for the production of vases than tea wares, but whether Duesbury would have agreed with Wedgwood that 'it was much the most profitable branch I ever launched into' we do not know.

There was always the search for new ideas and inspiration including engravings, which could be adapted by the modeller. It is interesting to note that in the reprint of extracts of the sale of 'Derby and Chelsea Porcelane', auctioned by Messrs Christie and Ansell in

May 1782 of 'superb Ornaments for Chimney Pieces, Toilets, etc. in Vases, Urns and Tripods', one of the lots described as 'An elegant Etruscan shape vase and pedestal' was bought by Wedgwood.[1]

Sometimes source books could be acquired from the London book dealers and print sellers, including 'French prints' bought from Sayer and Bennett:[2] other prints after Bouchardon, published by François Vivares and sold by Mrs Vivares at her print shop in Newport Street, were also purchased. Fig.46 was adapted from one of the Bouchardon designs; and the incense burner (Fig.53) was obviously taken from *La Vertueuse Athénienne*, painted by Joseph Marie Vien (1716-1809) and engraved by P. Filipart in 1765. Fig.54 is taken from *Suite de Vases* which were engraved by Vien's wife, Marie (1728-1805), in 1760.[3] Reference has been made (see p.32) to the Derby moulds now belonging to Messrs Copeland-Spode and a fired clay model of this pattern has also been found amongst them.[4]

Vases in various forms ranging from the Mayflower vases (Fig.48), which were produced in imitation of the Meissen *Schneeballen* wares, and the eel trap vase (Fig.45) which copied an earlier design produced at Chelsea, were intended to appeal to an already established market and without overextending the artists working at the factory. Opinion seems to be divided as to whether the painted decoration on the vase and cover in Fig.47 was done at the factory or carried out at one of the London decorating establishments.

The modelling of the garniture of three vases (Fig.49) has been attributed to John Bacon and is similar to the Sphinx vase at Syon House. Clifford[5] states that two vases made *c.*1772-3 during the Chelsea/Derby period, were copied from designs by J.F.J. Saly (1717-1776) which were etched by La Live de Jully in 1754, but he considers that this garniture may be taken from another source, as suggested by the title of the publication: *Première Suite des Vases Antiques d'apres Saly et autres*/à Paris chez Bassau, graveur, rue de Foin.

On major works which required specialist decorators it was common practice for different artists to decorate themes at which they excelled and on the vase in Fig.50 the landscape was probably painted by Zachariah Boreman, whilst the figure was painted by Richard Askew. At least three artists in addition to gilders are thought to have been engaged on the bough pot in Fig.56. At this time Angelica Kauffmann was one of the leading artists in England and engravings of her works were in great demand. So it was natural that copies of her work should be used by the Derby artists and it is thought that this version of her *Cupid being disarmed by Euphrosne* was painted as soon as the engraving, by Thomas Burke in 1784, was available.

Landscape painting at Derby reached a very high standard and the pot-pourri vase (Fig.57) is an example of the quality of this work. Yellow enamel was always expensive, as stated in the Lygo correspondence[6]. It was exceptionally scarce and could only be purchased in quantities of two or three ounces at a time it was therefore only natural that it would only be used on special high quality orders which would enhance the reputation of the factory.

1. Nightingale, (reprint 1973), *op. cit.* p.69.
2. Derby Public Record Office: Invoice, Sept.1st, 1774.
3. Clifford, 1978, *Some English Ceramic Vases and their Sources Part 1* . Trans. E.C.C., Vol.10, Pt.3, pps.159-173. Pls.75, 79, 80, 83 & 84.
4. Rowan 1988 *Derby Models Rediscovered, Antique Dealer & Collectors Guide,* May, p.56.
5. Clifford 1978, *op. cit.,* p.169.
6. Lygo correspondence—see Judith Anderson, p.20.

45. EEL TRAP VASE *c.*1765

Vase of oviform shape with a flared neck, resting on a flat base and with two handles moulded to represent bulrushes. The body of the vase moulded to represent the basket-work of a trap, with alternate cut-out narrow strips round the shoulder and the neck, four bands of moulded rope-work evenly spaced around the body, another round the neck and one round the rim, with moulded rope handles on the shoulder on both sides. Two geese on the apron base standing on one side of the vase and a nest containing three eggs on the apron base on the reverse.

The two geese painted in flamboyant enamel colours, with the bulrushes in green and dark purple flowers and the cord around the trap picked out in gilt.

Mark: Patch marks.

H. 22.9 cm.   Derby Museum & Art Gallery (493-1-61)

See: Victoria & Albert Museum (C.2994-1901)

Museum of London (C.1907 & 8-1913) for Chelsea examples.

Lit: Rackham, 1923, *op.cit.,* Pl.36, No.155, p.43, for Spode example *c.*1840, previously thought of as late Derby.

Rice, 1983, *op.cit.,* Pl.121, showing a pair 24.1 cm & 21.5 cm. dated *c.*1765-70.

Adams, 1987, *op.cit.,* Pl.94 for Chelsea example *c.*1758.

46. VASE AND COVER   *c.*1765

A slender cone-shaped vase with shoulders extended on both sides to form a loop handle with moulded leaf decoration on the apex and terminating in leaf moulding, with a narrow flared neck and domed shaped cover surmounted by a flower finial, set on an inverted ogee base with spreading foot.

Painted around the lower section of the vase and continuing up on the sides under the handles and on the foot, a ground of closely painted vertical alternate stripes in turquoise and dark blue. A floral bouquet and scattered sprays of flowers painted in naturalistic enamel colours on both sides of the white upper section, the neck and the cover of the vase, with gilt lines round the neck, foot and base and the handles outlined in gilt.

Mark: Patch marks and incised '20'.

H. 23.cm.   Derby Museum & Art Gallery (676-1980)

47. VASE AND COVER

(part of a garniture)   c.1758–60

Vase of tapering ovoid shape with short straight neck and with two elaborately shaped scroll handles with raised 'thumb rests', terminating at both ends with flowers moulded in relief, and a low domed cover decorated with flowers and leaves moulded in relief and surmounted by a floral bud. (The cover is wrong.)

This vase would have formed the central piece of a garniture of three vases, and the cover of this vase belongs to one of the side vases; the correct cover for the central vase is high domed.

Painted with a design of a boy holding a long pole, to which is attached a conical net held in a frame, standing on a bridge with two companions to assist him; a large bushy-topped tree on the opposite bank of the river, to which is tied a large net supported on poles, all reserved in a gilt panel on a mazarine-blue ground; the reverse panel depicting birds in flight. A gilt dentil border round the rim of the cover and the handles outlined in gilt.

Mark: Patch marks.

H. 25.5 cm.   Derby Museum & Art Gallery (504-1961)

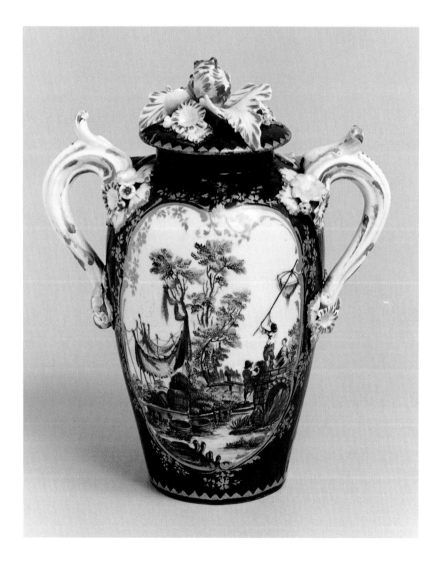

Note: in addition to this example there is another with a similar design in the British Museum. It has been suggested by Hodgson (1986, *Ceramics*, July/ August, p.107) that perhaps a more suitable title would be 'Fishers' and not 'Bird Catchers', but both the size and the shape of the net would have made it difficult to use in water. In many households songbirds were kept as pets and the birds were caught either in a cone-shaped net or by spreading birdlime on the branches of a tree.

See: Brighton Museum & Art Gallery, Willett Collection No.659 creamware jug and No.330 matching punch bowl, where part of the design, including the group of bird catchers and part of the large tree has been joined to a group of farm buildings and a haystack, transfer-printed in black. The punch bowl is inscribed 'Success to ye Eagle. John Lancefield Commander 1782'.

Lit: Bowles, 1786, *New and Enlarged Catalogue,* London. No.189, entitled 'The Bird Catcher'.

Hobson, 1905, *op. cit.,* IV, 3 for example in the British Museum with similar decoration.

Hurlbutt, 1933, *op. cit.,* Pl.IV.

Barrett & Thorpe, 1971, *op. cit.,* Pl.77 and p.28, where it is suggested that the decoration may be the work of an outside decorator.

Williams, 1973, *op.cit.,* for similar vase.

Twitchett, 1980, *op.cit.,* Pl.27 for garniture of three vases and covers. Here it is suggested that the decoration may have been carried out at the studio of Thomas Hughes of London.

Rice, 1983, *op.cit.,* Pl.132. On p.59 the suggestion that vases of this type were decorated in London, is mentioned but goes on to state that there is no concrete evidence to support this view.

Hodgson, 1986, *Fishers or Birdcatchers? Ceramics* July/August, p.101, Pl.2 for transfer-print used on a Worcester vase.

48. GARNITURE OF THREE MAYFLOWER VASES AND COVERS
c.1770-75

Quadrangular baluster shape with square-shaped neck and set on a square stepped-up plinth with applied *schneeballen* (may flowers), tightly packed moulded florets overlaid with branches bearing berries, (in imitation of Meissen *Schneeballen* wares.) A quadrangular-shaped domed cover surmounted by a pointed floral finial.

Painted in naturalistic enamel colours, green on the florets and red on the berries and gilt.

Central Vase 29 cm. Side Vase 24 cm.

Derby Museum & Art Gallery (108-2-1988)

Lit: Hurlbutt, 1933, *op.cit.,* Pl. VI for vases and *schneeballen* boxes and covers.

Bradley, 1978, *op.cit.,* Pl. 121 for similar shape without cover.

49. GARNITURE OF THREE VASES AND COVERS   *c.*1773

Central vase (stand missing)

Of double ogee shape with a bulbous ring round the central portion decorated with spiral straps, a band round the shoulder decorated with rosettes, the ribbed dome top and capstan-shaped neck matching the side vases, and the domed cover surmounted by an onion finial. Two mythological winged dragons, with lion legs and paws, a dog-like head with long jaws and small ears and long serpent-like tails covered in scales, one at each side of the pot; two moulded lion-head masks set centrally on the front and back of the pot with a chain of moulded husks looped behind their heads and supported on the sides by the curly tails of the dragons. Set on a high domed foot decorated with acanthus leaves and gadroon moulding round the base, attached to a square plinth, moulded with rams heads and hanging drapery suspended from rosettes.

Painted on a claret ground with a band of turquoise round the shoulder and decorated with gilt rosettes; the feet of the dragons, the husk chain and the onion finial in gilt and the raised moulded decoration all picked out in gilt.

The missing stand would have raised it to a more commanding position in the garniture.

Side vases and stands

Of ovoid shape set on a high foot, rising from a square plinth, with a ribbed, moulded dome top and capstan-shaped neck, surmounted by a small domed cover with a flame finial. Two female demi-figures, with the hind quarters of lions, squatting on the domed covers with their arms, terminating in paws, resting on the top of the capstan-shaped rim. Four masks set at equidistant intervals round the body of the vase and set between two rows of moulded ropes and cross-over ropes, above two rows of feather moulding round the base, above a square pedestal. The cut-out, shaped plinths moulded with four griffins terminating in rococo scrolls and pendant husks.

Painted on a claret ground with the ribbons fastening the ropes turquoise; the ropes, the flame finial, the beaks of the griffins and the husks all picked out in gilt and the demi-figures all gilt.

The modelling of these vases has been attributed to John Bacon.

Mark: Gold anchor on the central vase.

Central vase H. 31 cm. Side vases H. 36 cm.   Private Collection

See: Victoria & Albert Museum (Schr.1.248) for similar stands.

Exh: Burlington House Fair, 1985.

Lit: Clifford, 1978, *Some English Vases & Their Sources*. Trans. E.C.C., Vol.10, pt.3, Pls.80A & B.

Twitchett, 1987, *op.cit.,* Pl.7, p.75.

50. VASE AND COVER

Ovoid body with two handles in the form of winged female demi-figures, whose heads rise above the shoulder of the vase which is moulded with a band with, on either side of the vase, a mask flanked by two lions in relief, set above a moulded fret pattern, with a high foot rising from a square plinth. A domed top, obliquely gadrooned and a capstan-shaped neck surmounted by a domed cover with a cone-shaped finial.

Painted with an oval medallion on either side of the body, reserved on a ground of close vertical gilded stripes, with a landscape on one side and a figure on the reverse, with acanthus leaf decoration on the foot picked out in gilt. The demi-figures in 'biscuit'. Landscape probably painted by Zachariah Boreman and the figure by Richard Askew.

Mark: Patch marks. Incised No.86.

H. 39 cm.   Derby Museum & Art Gallery (74-1988)

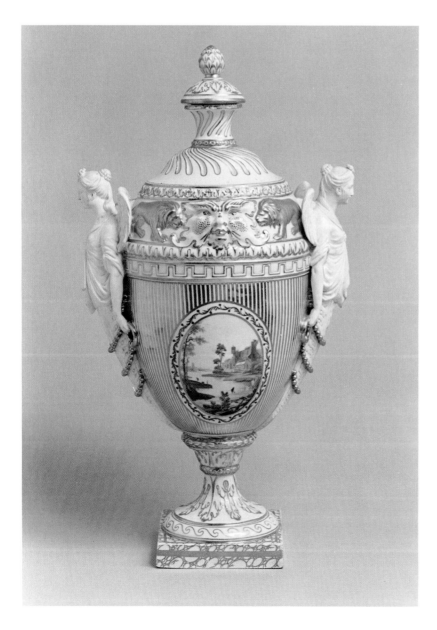

Note: Writing in *Ceramics* (Vol.V, August 1987), Twitchett states that the mark on the 'Gibraltar Vase' *c.*1782, exhibited at Burlington House Fair in September 1985, which is of similar shape and style to this vase, marks the introduction of 'crossed batons' between the 'Crown over D and six dots' mark. Twitchett, 1980, *op.cit.,* p.141, has pointed out that the difference in size of these vases would indicate that they would probably have formed the centrepiece for a *garniture de cheminée.*

See: Victoria & Albert Museum (C.825-1882) in the Jones Bequest.

Lit: Rackham, 1923, *op.cit.,* Pl.140 for later example.

Tapp, 1934, *Zachariah Boreman, Connoisseur* Vol.XCIII, January, pp.28-35 for reference to Boreman.

Tapp, 1934, *Richard Askew, Painter of Ceramics, Connoisseur,* Vol.XCIII, June, pp.359-363, for reference to Askew.

Austin, 1977, *op.cit.,* No.91, for reference to Askew's work.

Twitchett, 1980, *op.cit.,* Pls.152 & 153.

Twitchett, 1987, *Wm. Duesbury, A Man of Achievement, Ceramics* Vol.V, August, Pl.8, for vase depicting the Siege of Gibraltar, in 1782.

51.   EWER AND STAND

*c.*1785

Ovoid body with narrow neck and wavy shell-shaped lip and spout with imbricated loop handle, rising from a satyr's mask, with a flaring vertically fluted spreading foot, set on a square plinth, resting on a shaped stand moulded with rams heads at each of the corners and joined together by a moulded looped rope.

Painted on either side of the body an oval medallion surrounded by a dog-tooth border, reserved on a ground of closely painted vertical gilt stripes, with on one side a river landscape and on the reverse the figure of a woman, dressed in loose flowing drapery, dancing whilst playing a stringed instrument. With bands of 'Smith's lapis lazuli blue' and gilt, painted round the shoulder and the base of the neck, and with the handle, the foot and the pedestal all picked out in blue and gilt.

The painted landscape may be ascribed to Zachariah Boreman and the figure subject to Richard Askew.

Mark: Patch marks. Crown, crossed batons, six dots and 'D' in blue on the ewer; incised No. 92 on the base. Crown over 'D' in gilt, on the upper surface of the plinth. '5' in blue for ground layer, John Yates.

H. 29 cm.

Derby Museum & Art Gallery (Ewer -568-1-1962; Stand-1565-1)

See: Fig. 50 for references to Boreman and Askew.

Lit: Rackham, 1923, *op.cit.*, Pl.27, No.105 for similar shape.

Tapp, 1934, *op.cit.*, for references to Boreman and Askew.

Gilhespy, 1951, *op.cit.*, p.57, figs.101 and 102.

Barrett & Thorpe, 1971, *op.cit.*, Pl.118.

Austin, 1977, *op.cit.*, for references to Askew.

Bradley, 1978, *op.cit.*, Pls.34 and 35 for similar shape, forming part of a five set *garniture de cheminée*, and in the footnote it is stated that the figure of 'Maria', illustrating Sterne's *Sentimental Journey* is after a composition by Angelica Kauffmann, engraved in red stipple by W.W. Ryland, and published 12 April, 1779, after a composition engraved by Francesco Bartolozzi, 1780, illustrating a poem by George, Lord Lyttleton, in Vol.II, of Dodsley's *Collection of Poems by Several Hands*.

Twitchett, 1980, *op.cit.*, Pls.106, 168 & 169, described as 'Kedleston-shaped'.

Lippert, 1987, *op.cit.*, Cat. No.31, p.157 for similar shape.

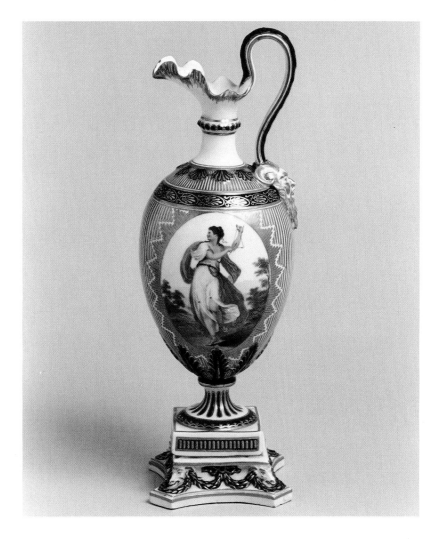

52. POT-POURRI VASE AND COVER (one of a pair)   *c.1770*

Vase of baluster shape, decorated with flowers in 'biscuit' moulded in relief, a tall neck, with cut-out holes in the shoulder, contracting into a narrow opening, then opening out with a wide, upturned, inverted rim, with small foliate leaf handles, set on a raised pedestal base with four scroll feet. A tall slightly concave cover with cut-out flutes and surmounted by a domed top and flower finial. The vase forms part of a *garniture de cheminée* of five pieces, consisting of three large and two smaller vases.

Painted on either side with cherubs in clouds in rose-pink *camaieu*, with the foliate leaf handles, the neck and pedestal stand and the cover painted in pea-green enamel and gold.

Cherubs probably painted by Richard Askew and the 'biscuit' flowers modelled by Stephan.

H. 29 cm.   Derby Museum & Art Gallery (109-1988)

See: Fig. 50 for reference to Askew's work.

Derby Museum & Art Gallery (612-1963) for two smaller vases without covers, H. 19 cm. decorated in a similar style.

Prov: Lord Kinnaird and Frank Hurlbutt Collections.

Lit: Duesbury London Sale 19 April, 1771, Lot 68.

Nightingale, 1881, *op. cit.,* pp.29, Lot 67. 'A jar, ornamented with flowers, after Nature; finely painted in Cupids, after Busha; and highly finish'd in burnish'd gold, and a fine pea-green ground £2. 1s.
  Lot 68. Two beakers, of the same elegance and beauty £2.19s'.

Hurlbutt, 1933, *op. cit.,* Pl.177.

Barrett & Thorpe, 1971, *op. cit.,* Pl.117.

Bradley, 1978, *op. cit.,* Pl.120, for undecorated smaller vase.

Rice, 1983, *op. cit.,* Pl. 136 for smaller vase, undecorated.

53. INCENSE BURNER *c.*1773-4

Large shallow bowl, terminating beneath the bowl in a pendant husk, with two moulded ring handles; a shallow perforated domed cover, surmounted by a pineapple finial. The bowl carried on a frame with circular upright sides, decorated with a running scroll motif and supported on three slightly tapering legs, starting at the shoulder with goats' heads moulded in relief in 'biscuit' and terminating in cloven hoofs, with a snake coiled spirally upwards and set between the legs of the stand. Set on a triangular-shaped base with a moulded pineapple set in the centre.

Taken from a painting by J.M. Vien (1716-1809) *Une Prétresse qui brûle de l'encens sur en trépied.* Exhibited Paris, 1763. Engraved by P. Filipart in 1765, entitled *La Vertueuse Athénienne.*

Painted on the shoulder of the bowl, the sides of the tripod support legs and the shaped base, in a distinctive blue enamel.

H. 22 cm. Derby Museum & Art Gallery (826-1986)

Lit: Eriksen & Watson, 1963, 'The "Athenienne" and the Revival of the Classical Tripod' *Burlington, Magazine,* No.720, Vol. CV, p.108 and Pls. 13 & 14, showing a tripod and incense burner which was made for King Stanislas of Poland, and has incised on the lid 'Fait par P. Caffieri à Paris En 1768'.

Clifford, 1978, *Some English Ceramic Vases and their Sources* Trans. E.C.C., Vol.10, Pt.3, p.171, Pl.84c.

Anderson, 1988, *op. cit.,* p.15, illustrates the 1773 W. Duesbury & Co. trade card, which depicts an incense burner in the bottom left-hand corner, as a candelabrum.

54. VASE (one of a pair, covers missing)   *c.*1770-75

Ovoid body with short concave neck and terminating at the base with a shaped inverted onion knob, supported by three caryatid figures who form part of ribbed loop handles, which rest on their heads, rising above the rim and the caryatids terminating downwards in lion paw feet which rest on a triangular-shaped plinth, set on a shaped pedestal. The body of the vase and the figures of the caryatids encrusted with flowers moulded in relief.

The body painted with an underglaze dark blue ground, the caryatids flesh-colour, with the flowers in naturalistic enamel colours. The top and the alternate rectangular panels on the plinth painted with gilt floral sprays on a white background and all picked out in gilt.

Mark: Patch marks.

H. 22.5 cm.   Derby Museum & Art Gallery (356-1982)

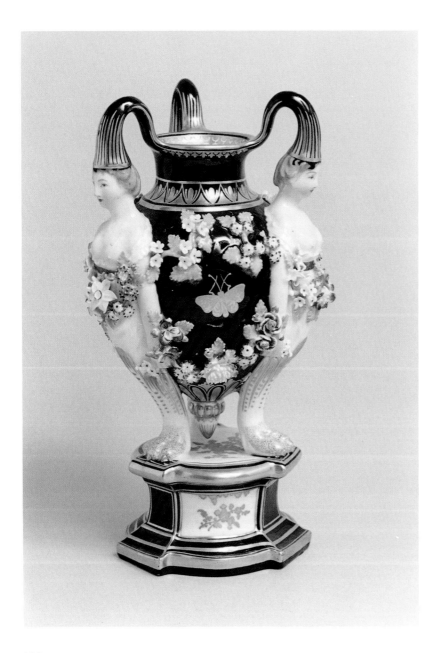

See: Victoria & Albert Museum (Schr. 1.239) for pair, with covers, which rest on a moulded circular pedestal and painted with trophies of arms *en grisaille.*

Lit: Rackham, 1928 (revised), *op. cit.,* Pl.30.

Clifford, 1978, *op. cit.,* p.171, Pl.83.

55. VASE

c.1765

Vase with short expanding fluted neck, truncated oviform body with urn-shaped foot, resting on a square plinth. Two scroll loop handles rising above the rim, and the upper part of the foot fluted; the body decorated with moulded vertical concave bands, with garlands of laurel suspended from the neck in alternate bands. Painted in turquoise blue enamel and white, in each alternate panel, and gilt.

Mark: Patch marks, incised 20.

H. 22.7 cm.   Derby Museum & Art Gallery (88)

See: Victoria & Albert Museum (Schr. 436).

56. BOUGH POT   *c.*1785

The pot D-shaped with *bombé* front and shell scroll handles at both ends, set on four rococo scroll feet; the top pierced with eighteen irregular shaped holes, fitting into the pot which stands on a shaped plinth with concave sides, repeating the outline shape of the pot.

Painted, on a pink background decorated with gilt stars, with a scene depicting Cupid being disarmed by Euphrosyne, on a grey background surrounded by seed-pearls, and pendant swags of roses on each side with on the reverse, a landscape in *grisaille,* set in a gilt frame. The stand painted to match the pot, with a gilt line round the top and base of the stand. The shell scroll handles and rococo feet outlined in gilt.

Probably painted by James Banford, William Billingsley and possibly Zachariah Boreman.

Cupid being disarmed by Euphrosyne is after a composition by Angelica Kauffmann and engraved by Thomas Burke in 1784.

Mark: Patch marks on stand. I (Gilder's mark – Thomas Soar). Incised 'star' on the pot. Incised triangle on the stand.

H. 12 cm. L. 17.5 cm.   Derby Museum & Art Gallery (368-1982).

See: Fig. 35 for reference to 'star' mark, and Fig. 37 for reference to 'triangle' mark.

Lit: Barrett & Thorpe, 1971, *op. cit.,* p.156 for reference to an entry in Duesbury's *London Account Book,* 27 September, 1786 'Sold to Mr. Mc.Carty, Cork, A large Center Vause No.86, enam'd with a subject of Cupid disarm'd by Euphrosine'.

Twitchett, 1980, *op. cit.,* Pl.158 for bough pot *c.*1775-80, and Pl.264 for slightly different shape *c.*1795-1800.

Chapel & Gere, 1985, *The Fine and Decorative Art Collections of Britain and Ireland,* London. p.154 for view of other side.

57. POT-POURRI VASE

*c.*1795

Vase trumpet-shaped with small shell-shaped handles and set on a waisted foot with spreading base; the domed cover pierced with six large and twelve small circular openings arranged in regular alternate positions, with a narrow neck and everted rim. Cover finial missing.

Painted on both sides, on a yellow ground, with a landscape in naturalistic enamel colours, surrounded by a shaped gilt frame with canted corners. The shell scroll handles picked out in gilt and a gilt line round the rim and foot of the vase and a similar gilt line round the edge, the rim and the holes of the cover.

Mark: Crown, crossed batons, six dots, and 'D' painted in puce.

H. 20 cm. Derby Museum & Art Gallery (248)

Lit: Rackham, 1923, *op. cit.*, Pl.33, No.136 for pot-pourri vase of similar shape, with finial cover.

Domestic Ware for the Tea Table

When non-alcoholic hot beverages were first known about in Europe, the only ceramic vessels which could be used to make or serve them in were of fairly unsophisticated earthenware and it was the desire to produce something more elegant, in imitation of the Chinese porcelain which was then beginning to pour into Europe, that acted as a spur to local production. Since the tea was being imported from China it was natural that the shapes of both the pots and the drinking cups should follow their designs. These are now called tea bowls but in the eighteenth century when the orders for them were sent by the merchants to China they were described as 'cups without handles' to distinguish them from ordinary cups with handles.

At this time both the tea itself and the drinking vessels were expensive and it was not long before those who could afford the luxury were anxious to display their possessions. Though the tea ceremony was neither so elaborate nor so formal as in Japan or China, English social habits were changed and a certain hour in the day was set aside for tea. The handleless cups also posed the problem as to how they should be held and in contemporary paintings some people are seen holding the bowl with the thumb supporting the footrim and the finger on the rim, whilst others preferred to hold it by wrapping finger and thumb around the rim.

Saucers too were a problem as, copying the oriental design, they were made without a well, and so as to steady the cup a raised gallery, called a *trembleuse* (Fig.88) was built up. Another device was to set the cup in a deep well in the saucer (Fig.84), but the idea of a shallow central well, though made at Bow[1] in the early 1760s, does not seem to have found favour in England and in a letter from Lygo dated 19 September, 1788, he repeated the comment of the Duchess of Devonshire 'that all the French pieces had sockets in their saucers'.

It is presumed that tea ware must have been produced during the 'dry-edge' period (1750-56) but none has survived which can, with certainty, be ascribed to this period. So far as Derby teapots are concerned, the earliest recorded has an incised date of 1756.[2] It is globular and four lobed and similar teapots can be seen in the Derby Museum & Art Gallery and the Castle Museum, Norwich.[3] A similar quatrefoil shape can be seen in a bowl (Fig.63) and a cup (Fig.65). A saucer matching the cup is illustrated in colour in the Derby Porcelain International Society Journal,[4] where it is stated that saucers of this shape are rare. One great advantage of this shape was that it gave the decorators a comparatively large flat space on which to paint their designs, which consisted chiefly of Chinese scenes, again reflecting oriental influence, or were taken from nature, depicting birds and insects, all drawn with great accuracy. This shape was followed by pots with vertical fluting (Fig.62) and although by c.1765, the characteristic moulded leaf on the upper section of the spout had given way to a

painted representation, this style of decoration remained popular.

At a later date *cabaret* or *déjeuner* sets became popular and the pot in Fig. 58 would have formed part of a set which would have included a tray.[5]

Even though the factory had been making pots for many years it was some time before they were able to produce a paste which was capable of overcoming the heat expansion problem. 'Flying pots' which exploded were Lygo's single biggest embarrassment and letters of complaint sent to Duesbury in the late 1780s are amongst the earliest in his surviving correspondence: he 'wished something could be done respecting the teapots to prevent them flying, for the disgrace is worse than anything and it looses the sale of many sets'. And in another letter of 26 March, 1789, he reported he was quite distressed about daily complaints of teapots flying.

Whether for this reason customers preferred to use silver teapots is not stated, but in the Sales Ledger[6] in the British Museum covering the period 1794-5, there are several orders for complete tea sets excluding the teapot. Coffee pots are rarely mentioned in the Ledger and it would seem that few were produced during this later period, though many more seem to have survived from the 1756-65 period than teapots. Could this have been due to the fact that coffee was a less popular drink and coffee pots were therefore less frequently used? Or were they chocolate pots, a drink more popular in France than in England, a beverage that was made at a lower temperature, and therefore less likely to cause the pot to 'fly'?

'Wish-bone' shaped handles were popular at Derby during the early period as can be seen on one cup (Fig. 65) and were still being used on the teapot (Fig.61) of a later date. Whereas another cup (Fig.64) with a butterfly-wing handle, though probably copied from the Chinese, is only found on cups of this shape and it is only in recent years that these have been accepted as Derby.

Outline drawings of different cup shapes are illustrated by Twitchett.[7] Unfortunately there is no record of the order passed to Derby for the set of breakfast 'basons' and saucers which carry the royal cypher 'G.R.', and, due to the monarch's shaky hand, have a raised *trembleuse* ring in the centre of the saucer (Fig.68). But in the Sales Ledger[8] there is an order dated 1 September, 1794:

> Sold to the Prince of Wales:-
> 1 Bell-shaped breakfast cup with handle and stand, enam'[d] with his Crest and blue and gold border   £1,11, 6.
> 2 Cream ewers, blue & gold   14. 0.
> 1 Slop bowl   10. 6
>   £2.16. 0.

These may have been replacements for an order in an earlier Sales Ledger, when the Prince had been granted an increase of £10,000 in his allowance by Parliament, which was intended to enable him to clear some of his outstanding and very substantial debts, but was used by him to effect new purchases.

Following the closure of the Nottingham Road factory in 1848, some of the Derby pattern books, a Plate Book and a Teaware Book were no longer required, and were disposed of to R.W. Binns and presented by him to the Worcester Royal Porcelain Company. To call them books is a misnomer, for they are in fact a collection of loose leaves. To complicate the matter there are what might be called two 'editions', one an 'original' and one a 'duplicate' which was discovered at Worcester by Henry Sandon in 1970. It was then found that artists/decorators names which had been pencilled in against certain patterns in the 'original' had been omitted from the 'duplicate' perhaps meaning that when the duplicate copy was assembled, those men were no longer working at the factory. However, this does not account for the fact that in some cases the two sets differ in their pattern numbers.

There is also another pattern book, in the British Museum, which formed part of the Paget Bequest and is later in date, with the patterns painted on the pages of the book. It is thought that this copy may have been retained by the group of potters that established a factory in King Street, Derby, and which continued in existence until taken over by the Royal Crown Derby in 1935. The documents were presented to the British Museum in the following year by F. Howard Paget, proprietor of the King Street factory since 1917.

Twitchett,[9] in discussing the origin of the pattern books at Worcester, states 'there is however, some evidence for believing that John Duesbury ... drew up the majority of patterns', but omits to state whether this refers to both editions. John Duesbury was a relative of William Duesbury, possibly a younger brother or nephew. He worked at the factory, first as a gilder (being allocated 12 in the list of gilder's marks) and later becoming foreman and time keeper. In the biographies of painters and gilders working at the factory, no dates for him are mentioned. However, it is reasonable to suppose that as he would have been fully employed as a gilder and, if he is responsible for the pattern book, it could not therefore have been done prior to his becoming foreman. He was still working as a gilder when he put his number on the breakfast bason and saucer (Fig.68) which is thought to date from *c.*1785.

There are no dates on any of the pattern books and in his article Twitchett states 'the few remnant patterns which survive from what was probably the first book'[10] and goes on to date these from about 1775, whilst the majority of those included in the pattern books date from the early 1780s. The cup (Fig.73) dated *c.*1775, is pattern 1, which would seem to back up this statement. It is not clear if any system of pattern marking was in use before this date — which coincided roughly with the date that Lygo was appointed Duesbury's London agent and took charge of the London showroom.

It has also been suggested that the pattern books were begun at Lygo's suggestion, but there is nothing in his surviving correspondence to indicate that a duplicate copy was available for clients to study in the London showroom. Neither can one be sure that the copy at the factory was available for the use of customers since when the Duchess of Devonshire visited the factory Stables, who was then in charge, could only produce a set of cups ordered by the Duke of Bedford for her to inspect.

Barrett & Thorpe[11] suggest that they may represent an attempt, at a later date, to bring together a mass of scattered drawings which were originally produced as day to day instructions to the artist-craftsmen concerned. However, Twitchett[12] considers this opinion to be without foundation and quotes a 1786 order which specifies the pattern number, and in most of the orders in the Sales Ledgers the pattern number is given.[13] This was not done in every case and there are occasionally entries in the Sales Ledger where a sketchy description of the decoration had to be written out, — instructions that would not have been needed if there were pattern numbers for every design or border pattern.

At other times, instead of a number, Lygo states 'To match...' giving the name of a client's previous order as on 3 February 1791 '4 or 6 sets Mr Hogg's pattern' and on 7 July 1790 he wrote reporting Mrs Gordon had requested 'Her pattern not to be copied anymore' leaving it to the factory to work out which pattern she wished to retain for her exclusive use. Whilst in another letter dated January 1789, Lygo wrote complaining he 'had never had two "tea pattern 100" sets alike, for some had more sprigs on in proportion to their size'.

Although most writers tend to agree with the starting date of the pattern books — John[14] 1780; Barrett and Thorpe[15] 'from about 1782'; all fail to agree on a closing date. Twitchett[16] gives the date $c.1805$ but later[17] changes this to $c.1810$; John states 1810-12; and Barrett & Thorpe 'about 1820' and go on to point out 'For some reason unknown, pattern numbers ceased to be put on wares after the painted mark was superseded by the printed mark'.

Further confusion was added by Haslem[18] when he stated 'The patterns in the books are all numbered and it was the custom, seldom departed from, to mark the corresponding numbers on the bottoms of the pieces on which the patterns were severally done'. It should be remembered however, that he did not start working at the factory until 1822 and therefore when he wrote this, in 1875, he had no personal knowledge of the earlier period on which to base his remark. Here the only pieces marked with a pattern number are: Fig.68, $c.1785$, pattern 331; Fig.71, $c.1775$, pattern 11; Fig.73, $c.1775$, pattern 1; Fig.75, $c.1790$-95, pattern 77; Fig.89, $c.1790$, pattern 221 and a reference to a similar piece in the Derby Pattern Book with the number 236. Others carry no numbers, though matching pieces in the set could have been marked with a number.

It should also be remembered that none of the painted decoration on any of these pieces was signed by the artists and attributions therefore can only be given on stylistic grounds. In some cases in the 'original' pattern book, an artist's name is written against a pattern, but in cases where it might be necessary for more than one artist to decorate a large set, this would be done by a team, all working in a similar manner.

Some of the pieces (Fig.89) produced were bought not for use but for display. There had long been a European tradition of displaying pieces of interest in china galleries and although they generally consisted mostly of oriental ceramics, gradually European and then English factories would have been represented in collections. China cabinets could be filled with smaller pieces and many of the wares produced at this time by Derby were designed for display rather than use.

The Duesbury II period (1786-97) is considered by many collectors today as the peak period in the factory's history and certainly the high standard of the decoration on the tea wares painted by the leading ceramic artists of the day such as Askew (Fig.80), Boreman (Fig.82 & Fig.84), Complin (Fig.89), Withers (Fig.93) and Billingsley (Fig.89 & 96) was superior to any being produced at that time by any other factory in England.

Cow Creamers

Although the idea for a creamer in the form of a cow was based on a silver model first produced in England in 1753, the ceramic version did not become popular until the nineteenth century, when it was taken up by the Staffordshire potters and also at the King Street Derby factory. However, eighteenth century examples do survive, principally some tortoiseshell ones, and some of the so-called 'Pratt-type' cow creamers which date from before 1800.

Mugs

Describing the work of the artist decorator William Dixon, who was at Derby for a short time between 1820 and 1823, Haslem[20] states that his work was usually painted on large-sized porter mugs; and in his article[21] Anthony Hoyte takes the term 'porter mugs' to refer to quart mugs and goes on to state that their most prolific production was from about 1805 to 1830. He also admits that the origin of the name 'porter mug' is obscure. In the Sales Ledger Vol.3, 1791[22] there are references to the sales of 'quart toast mugs' and perhaps this is a more correct name. At that time it was considered beneficial for ones health to drink water that had been flavoured by immersing a piece of toast in it, whereas porter, a dark brown malt beverage, supposedly so-called because it was a favourite drink with the London porters, had to be drunk within a few days of production before becoming sour and undrinkable. This could be done if there were a local brewery, or if the liquid were brewed at home, but not otherwise. The mug in Fig.95 pre-dates those listed in the Sales Ledger and there is also an

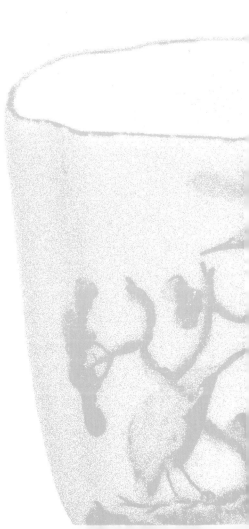

example of this Pattern No.53, in the British Museum,[23] so perhaps this one should be described more correctly as a 'Quart toast mug' and not a 'Porter mug'. The example in the Victoria & Albert Museum with the same rare 'DK' mark *c*.1795 is described as a mug.

Confiture set

In the past, these sets (Fig.96) have frequently been described, out of ignorance, as either 'toilet jars' or 'jam jars', but as Gage & Marsh[24] have pointed out, there is a reference in the Sèvres archives to '*pots à confiture*' and until the French Revolution in 1789, a '*pot à confiture*' attached to a '*plateau Herbert, 'ovale'* or '*du Roi*' would have formed part of a large dessert service. And by being attached in this way to the tray, were quite different from the '*pots à pommade*' or the '*pots à tabac*'.

References
1. Adams & Redstone, 1981, *Bow Porcelain* Pls.96 & 99 for breakfast cup and saucer with central well.
2. Cecil Higgins Museum, Bedford (C.364).
3. Bradley, 1978, *op. cit.* p.49.
4. *Derby Porcelain International Society*. Journal 1. Colour Pl.1.
5. Gilhespy, 1961, *Derby Porcelain*, Pl.95, on a pink ground.
6. The British Museum, *The William Bemrose Collection of Papers* Sales Ledger Vol.4.
7. Twitchett, 1980, *op.cit.* p.93.
8. The British Museum, *op. cit.*, Sales Ledger Vol.5.
9. Twitchett, 1971, *The Old Derby Pattern Books*. Collectors Guide. September p.70.
10. Twitchett, 1971, *op. cit.*, p.70.
11. Barrett and Thorpe, 1971, *Derby Porcelain*. p.118.
12. Twitchett, 1980, *op. cit.*, p.85.
13. The British Museum, *op. cit.*, Sales Ledger Vol. 5.
14. John, 1963, *William Billingsley 1758-1828, The Connoisseur*. February.
15. Barrett and Thorpe, 1971, *op. cit.*, p.117.
16. Twitchett, 1971, *op. cit.*, p.70.
17. Bradley, 1978, *op. cit.*, p.145.
18. Haslem, 1881 (1973 reprint), *op. cit.*, p.185.
19. Twitchett, 1976, *op. cit.*, p.34, ill. 75.
20. Haslem, 1973, *op. cit.*, p.118.
21. Hoyte, 1987, *Splendour on Display, The Antique Dealer and Collectors Guide*, March, pps. 40-43.
22. The British Museum, *op. cit.*, Sales Ledger Vol.3.
23. The British Museum, *op. cit.*, Sales Ledger Vol.3.
24. Gage and Marsh, 1988, *Tobacco Containers & Accessories*. p.45 & Pls.28, 30 & 31.

58. CABARET TEAPOT AND COVER   *c.*1780

Small cabaret teapot of globular shape with S-shaped spout and ear-shaped handle, with a low domed cover and flattened onion finial.

Painted round the top of the pot and on the cover with a pattern of reticulated gilding, on a green wash band divided by shaped blanks with a trailing garland of roses, a gilt line painted round the base, shoulder and neck on the pot, with the edge of the handle, the tip of the spout and the onion finial all outlined in gilt.

Mark: Crown over 'D' in puce on the tray, cup and saucer, but not on teapot.

H. 12 cm.   Derby Museum & Art Gallery (272)

Lit: Twitchett, 1980, *op. cit.,* Pl.107 for similar shape teapot.

See: A watercolour of one of the land-scapes entitled *On Breadsall Common* is in the Derby Museum Collection.

Lit: Haslem, 1876, *op. cit.,* p.190, where the decoration is ascribed to Moscrop, but this is now doubted.

Bemrose, 1898, Catalogue, Derby. Pl.IV.

Rackham, 1923, *op. cit.,* Pl.161, p.45, for similar shape.

Bradley, 1978, *op. cit.,* Pl.252, for cup and saucer decorated with this pattern.

Twitchett, 1980, *op. cit.,* Pl.179, for similar shape.

Miller & Berthoud, 1985, *An Anthology of British Teapots,* Wingham, Kent. Pl.352, p.59, for similar shape.

Teapot of globular shape, with curved spout moulded with basket weave and leaf decoration round the lower part, and a loop handle with moulded thumb rest. A domed cover surmounted by a ring finial held in an upright position by a moulded ceramic rivet.

Painted in enamel colours with swags of flowers supported by gilt rosettes and intersected by stylised leaf decoration painted in pale blue and purple, with a single flower stem painted green growing up on each side from the base of the handle and the spout, flanking a central reserve depicting a rural landscape. A border of gilt dots set between two gilt lines above a row of arrow-heads forming a band round the shoulder of the pot, a gilt chain decoration on the handle and a gilt line round the rim, the base, the tip of the spout and the edge of the handle. The cover painted with swags of flowers supported by gilt rosettes, scattered ribbons tied in bows and a similar arrow-head border surrounding the gilt finial. Pattern No. 320 in the Derby Pattern Book.

Mark: Crown, crossed batons, six dots and 'D' painted in puce enamel. Stilt marks. '3' (Gilder's mark — William Cooper, Jnr). Impressed GXXO.

H. 16.5 cm.   Derby Museum & Art Gallery (1399)

60. TEAPOT, COVER AND STAND   *c.1775–82*

Cylindrical shape, tapering towards the foot, with sloping shoulders and pierced gallery round the rim, a flat angled handle with pierced moulding at the upper terminal and the lower end attached to the body with a moulded ceramic rivet. A curved spout with basket weave and leaf moulding round the lower part. A low domed cover with fluted moulding and a sphinx terminal. The stand of cylindrical form with steeply rising flange, on a flat base.

Painted in enamel colours with a mazarine-blue band below the shoulder and above the foot, a chain of elongated arrow-heads suspended from moulded rosettes, with scattered flowers round the shoulder and on the spout; the edge of the handle, tip of the spout, rim of the gallery and the spiral moulding round the foot, all picked out in mazarine blue. The stand decorated to match with a mazarine blue border round the up-turned edge. Smear glaze round the up-turned edge.

Mark: Crown over 'D' in blue enamel.

H. 14.5 cm.   Derby Museum & Art Gallery (1444)

Prov: Henry Evans Collection.

See: Fig. 71, for matching cup and saucer.

Lit: Bradley, 1978, *op. cit.*, Pl.233 for similar shape.

Miller & Berthoud, 1985, *op. cit.*, Pl.273, p.46 for similar shape.

See: Victoria & Albert Museum (C.251-1922) for similar shape.

Lit: Tilley, 1957, *Teapots and Tea,* Newport, Pl.27, No.85 for similar shape.

Barrett & Thorpe, 1971, *op. cit.,* Pl.108.

Bradley, 1978, *op. cit.,* Pl.235 for similar shape.

Graham & Oxley, 1981, *op. cit.,* Pl.32 for similar shape.

Miller & Berthoud, 1985, *op. cit.,* Pl.266.

61. TEAPOT AND COVER   *c.*1775-85

Globular shape with wish-bone handle and slightly curved crab-stock spout; a low domed cover surmounted by an onion knop.

Painted in enamel colours with spray of flowers on either side and on the underside of the spout, with scattered floral sprigs on the handle and the cover. A gilt dentil border round the rim of the pot and the edge of the cover, and a gilt line round the base, the tip of the spout and the edge of the handle.

Mark: Entwined Anchor and 'D' in gold.

H. 11 cm.   Derby Museum & Art Gallery (860-1895)

62. COFFEE POT AND COVER   *c.1765*

Baluster shape with vertical fluting, ribbed S-shaped spout and flat scroll
handle, a domed cover and spinning-top finial also fluted.

Painted in enamel colours in the chinese manner with, on one side three
people on a terrace, and on the other, a child holding a parasol over a lady
standing in a garden.

Mark: Patch marks.

H. 24.5 cm.   Derby Museum & Art Gallery (505-61)

Exh: Morley College, London, 1976.

Lit: Barrett & Thorpe, 1971, *op. cit.*,
Pl.38.

Bradley, 1978, *op. cit.*, Pl.61.

Lit: Barrett & Thorpe, 1971, *op. cit.*, Pl.2, p.8.

Bradley, 1978, *op. cit.*, Pl.67 for similar style of painting.

63. BOWL   *c.*1756

Quatrefoil shape, on a shallow circular base, with applied prunus sprigs and flowers, moulded with more than four petals and raised crinkled edge. Painted on all four sides with butterflies and insects.

During this early period, the names of the artists working in the factory are unknown. The so-called 'cotton-stalk' painter is frequently mentioned in the literature, but the varying accuracy with which butterflies, moths and insects are painted, in addition to the different species of birds, would indicate the work of more than one artist.

Mark: Ground base.

H. 6.5 cm. L. 9.8cm.   Derby Museum & Art Gallery (435-1-60)

64. CUP   *c.*1760

Bell shape with undulating rim and flat butterfly-wing handle, with four irregular shaped holes.

Painted in enamel colours with a design derived from the Chinese *famille verte,* with vertical and petal-shaped panels of flowers within a zig-zag cross-hatched border.

H. 7 cm.   Derby Museum & Art Gallery (634-2-64)

See: Victoria & Albert Museum (C.1054-1924) for similar cup.

Lit: Hodgson, 1906, *How to Identify Old China,* London. Pl. XXII, with saucer, as Liverpool.

Marshall, 1954, *Coloured Worcester Porcelain of the First Period, 1751-1783,* Newport. Pl.174 for similar shape, with saucer, as Worcester.

Tilley, 1957, *Teapots and Tea,* Pl. LXVI, fig. 199 a & b.

Spero, 1970, *op. cit.,* p.194 for similar shape with saucer.

Williams, 1973, *op. cit.,* Pl.74 for similar cup and saucer.

Bradley, 1978, *op. cit.,* Pl.70 for similar cup.

65. CUP   *c.*1756

Quatrefoil shape, with wishbone handle.

Painted in enamel colours with, on one side a bittern perched on the branch of a tree and another in flight, and on the reverse a moth and insect.

H. 5.7 cm.   Derby Museum & Art Gallery (420-44-69)

Lit: Bradley, 1978, *op. cit.,* Pl.65.

Graham & Oxley, 1981, *op. cit.,* Pl.12.

Lit: Barrett & Thorpe, 1971, *op. cit.*, Pl.109.

Bradley, 1978, *op. cit.*, Pl.264 for similar style of decoration on a *sucrier* in Derby Museum (1407-1).

66. TEA BOWL *c.*1780

Bowl moulded with shallow spiral flutes, shanked from right to left.

Painted on alternate flutes in underglaze blue and iron-red enamel, after a Chinese original. Known as the 'whorl' pattern.

Mark: Entwined Anchor and 'D' in gilt.

H. 4.8 cm. Derby Museum & Art Gallery (297)

Lit: Gilhespy, 1951, *op. cit.*, Fig.28.

67. TEA BOWL *c.*1770

Bowl moulded with sixteen shallow vertical flutes and serrated rim. The vertical flutes painted in pairs with pendant sprays of green leaves and flowers on a white background, and gilt leaves on a claret ground, with the ridge separating each flute and the rim of the bowl outlined in gilt.

Mark: Ground foot rim.

H. 4.3 cm. Derby Museum & Art Gallery (269)

68. BREAKFAST BASON AND SAUCER *c.*1785

The bason (sic) of cup shape, rising from the outer edge of the foot rim, with an elongated ear-shaped handle. The saucer, with a steeply rising rim and a raised *trembleuse* ring in the centre into which the bason fits.

The bason painted with a wreath of stylised leaves and ferns in gilt on a white background set between two broad bands painted yellow; and placed opposite the handle, surrounded by a circular gilt line, on a white background 'G R' in gold, surmounted by a Royal Crown painted in claret and gilt. With traces of gilt pendant border round the inside of the bason. A broad yellow band set between gilt lines on the saucer and the raised *trembleuse* ring outlined in gilt.

There is however, no record amongst the Royal Archives at Windsor of purchases made from the Derby Manufactory for this service.

Mark: Crown, crossed batons, six dots and 'D' in puce. Stilt marks. '12' (Gilder's mark — Jno.Duesbury). Impressed 'G' on the saucer. Pattern no.331 on saucer.

Bason H.7 cm. D. 9 cm. Saucer D. 15 cm.

Derby Museum & Art Gallery (Bason 252, Saucer 247)

See: Powis Castle (National Trust) for twelve pieces forming part of this service where it is stated they had belonged to George, 2nd Earl of Powis, and had been used when George III breakfasted with the Earl at Weymouth.

Lit: *Gentleman's Magazine* October, 1799 and 29 September, 1800, for references to Their Majesties meeting Earl Powis, who commanded the Shropshire Regiment of Militia, at Weymouth.

69. COFFEE CUP AND SAUCER   *c.*1775

Cup of standard Derby shape with plain loop handle, moulded with an embossed pattern of prunus blossom with one bird perched on a branch and another in flight, with similar moulded decoration on the saucer.

Painted with a band of Smith's blue round the rim of the cup and saucer and a gilt dentil border and a gilt floret on the inside of the cup and a gilt line round the outside of the footrim. Similar style decoration on the saucer, with a gilt floret in the centre.

Mark: Entwined Anchor and 'D' in gold.

Stilt marks. Ground foot rim.

Cup H. 6.5 cm. Saucer D. 12 cm.   Derby Museum & Art Gallery (59)

70. COFFEE CUP AND SAUCER   *c.*1770

Cup of tapering cone-shape with plain loop handle.

Painted with three florets scattered at irregular intervals on both the cup and the saucer, with an interlocking blue and gilt chain round the outside of the cup and the saucer and a matching blue line round the base of the cup and the well-head of the saucer.

Mark: Crown over 'D' in blue enamel.

Cup H. 5.5 cm. Saucer D. 11.5 cm.   Derby Museum & Art Gallery (212)

71. CUP AND SAUCER   *c.*1775

Cup with slightly tapering sides, above a lower section moulded with a fluted sunflower decoration, with a flat angular handle with moulded husk decoration and attached with moulded ceramic rivets.

Painted with wreaths of flowers set between swags of pendant husks, with similar decoration on the saucer.

Pattern No. 11.

Mark: Crown over 'D' in blue enamel.

Cup H. 5 cm. Saucer D. 13cm.   Derby Museum & Art Gallery (258a)

72. CUP   *c.*1775

Shaped as Fig.71.

Pattern No.54.

Mark: Crown, crossed batons and 'D' in purple.

H. 5 cm.   Derby Museum & Art Gallery (232)

Prov: J. Haslem Collection.

See: Fig.60 for similar pattern.

Victoria & Albert Museum (C.2074-1901) for similar cup.

Royal Museum, Canterbury for cup with a medallion profile set in the wreath.

Lit: Haslem, 1876, *op. cit.,* Pl. IV.

Gilhespy, 1951, *op. cit.,* Fig. 23.

Barrett & Thorpe, 1971, *op. cit.,* Pl.119b.

Twitchett, 1980, *op. cit.,* Pl.155 for matching teapot.

Berthoud, 1982, *An Anthology of British Cups,* Wingham, Pl.165 for similar shaped cup.

Lit: Bradley, 1978, *op. cit.*, Pl.244 for similar shape.

Berthoud, 1982, *op. cit.*, Pl.123 for similar style but with alternate acanthus leaves of different length made by Neale.

73. COFFEE CUP AND SAUCER   *c*.1775

Cup of standard Derby shape, with shallow spiral flutes shanked from right to left and moulded acanthus leaves, all of equal length, and a plain loop handle. The saucer moulded with a matching pattern.

Decorated with a gilt dentil border round the rim of the cup and edge of the saucer, with a gilt line round the centre of the saucer and the handle gilt.

Pattern No.1.

Mark: Crown, crossed batons and 'D' in puce. 27 impressed on cup; 8 on cup (Gilder – Wm.Longdon); 4 on saucer (Gilder – Wm.Yates).

Cup H. 6.3 cm. Saucer D. 13 cm.

Derby Museum & Art Gallery (57-1974)

74. TEA BOWL AND SAUCER   *c*.1775

Tea bowl moulded with a chain of flower heads, set between a running scroll border and moulded decoration of florets, with matching moulded decoration on the saucer.

Decorated with a gilt dentil border round the rim of the bowl and edge of the saucer and a gilt line round the foot-rim of the bowl and the centre of the saucer.

Mark: entwined Anchor and 'D' in gold.

Bowl H. 5 cm. Saucer D. 13 cm.   Derby Museum & Art Gallery (41)

75. TEA BOWL AND SAUCER   *c.*1790-95

Tea bowl of standard Derby cup shape.

Painted in the style of eighteenth century textile weaving known as 'IKAT', in puce, green, red and blue on the outside of the bowl and on the saucer, with a gilt line entwined about with a wreath of leaves and a 'Chantilly' sprig in the centre of the bowl and on the saucer and a gilt dentil border round the rim of the bowl and edge of saucer.

Pattern No. 77.

Mark: Crown, crossed batons and 'D' in purple. Impressed 'R' on saucer.

Bowl H. 6cm. Saucer D. 14 cm.   Derby Museum & Art Gallery (1449)

See: Derby Museum (170) for creamer shaped as Fig. 90, same decoration.

High Museum, Atlanta, Georgia for ice pail, cover and liner with similar style decoration.

Prov: Haslem Collection.

Lit: Godden, 1969, *The Illustrated Guide to Lowestoft Porcelain,* London. Pl.46, for similar ribbed moulded decoration.

76. COFFEE CUP AND SAUCER   *c.1770*

Cup moulded with vertical ribbed decoration, leaving a plain band near the rim, with a plain strap handle. The saucer moulded with matching decoration.

Painted with a wreath of flower heads on the smooth band round the top of the cup and a floret on the inside, with a gilt dentil border round the rim, a line round the foot rim and the handle outlined in gilt. The saucer decorated with a matching pattern.

Mark: Entwined Anchor and 'D' in gold.

Cup H. 6 cm. Saucer D. 13 cm.   Derby Museum & Art Gallery (28)

Lit: Berthoud, 1982, *op. cit.,* Pl.121 for matching shape and rose decoration and Pl.122, for matching border.

77. COFFEE CUP AND SAUCER   *c.1770*

Cup moulded with sixteen shallow flutes, shanked from right to left, with slightly serrated edge and acanthus fronds of alternate length, and a plain strap handle. The saucer moulded with matching decoration.

Painted with a border of Smith's blue overlaid with gilt florets round the rim of the cup and the edge of the saucer, with scattered floral sprays on the cup and saucer on which one spray is centrally placed, surrounded by a circular blue line on the saucer.

Mark: Entwined Anchor and 'D' in gold. Ground foot rim on cup only.

Cup H. 7 cm. Saucer D. 13 cm.   Derby Museum & Art Gallery (61)

78. COFFEE CUP AND SAUCER   *c.*1775–80

Cup of ogee shape with entwined loop handle.

The cup painted in naturalistic enamel colours with a rose in full bloom,
surrounded by leaves and other scattered roses and flowers, all set on a
ground base of thin slightly spiral gilt lines, with a gilt dentil border
round the rim and the handle picked out in gilt. A matching pattern on
the saucer, with a formal scalloped border round the inside well and a gilt
dentil border round the rim.

See: Victoria & Albert Museum
(C.703-1919) for similar cup and
saucer.

Mark: Crown over 'D'

Cup H. 6.5 cm. Saucer D. 13 cm.   Derby Museum & Art Gallery (62)

Lit: Gilhespy, 1951, *op. cit.,* Fig.25.

79. COFFEE CUP AND SAUCER   *c.*1770

Cup of standard Derby shape, moulded with vertical convex ribs,
serrated edge and plain loop handle. The saucer moulded to match.

Painted with a continuous chain band, outlined in brown on white, set
on a broad turquoise band round the upper section.

Mark: Crown over 'D' in blue. Stilt marks.

Cup H. 6.5 cm. Saucer D. 13 cm.   Derby Museum & Art Gallery (271)

Lit: Gilhespy, 1951, *op. cit.,* Fig.24.

Lit: Tapp, 1934, *op. cit.*, pp.359-363.

Austin, 1977, *op. cit.*, No. 91.

Bradley, 1978, *op. cit.*, Pl.248 for matching cup in City of Bristol Museum and Art Gallery (4041a).

80. SAUCER   *c.*1780

Of standard Derby shape.

Painted *en camaieu* with a draped cherub reclining on clouds, set in the centre of the saucer, with a garland of green leaves suspended from bows, picked out in gilt. A gilt line round the edge of the saucer and round the outside of the foot rim.

Cherub probably painted by Richard Askew.

Mark: Entwined Anchor and 'D' in gold. Ground foot rim.

D. 13 cm.   Derby Museum & Art Gallery (43)

81. TEA BOWL AND SAUCER   *c.*1770

Tea bowl of ogee shape, moulded with alternating concave and convex vertical flutes with an undulating rim. The saucer moulded with matching decoration and a scalloped edge.

Painted in naturalistic enamel colours with a floral bouquet placed in a central position on the tea bowl and surrounded by scattered floral sprigs and a gilt dentil border round the rim. With matching floral decoration on the saucer and a gilt dentil border round the scalloped edge.

Mark: Entwined Anchor and 'D' in gold. Ground foot rim.

Bowl H. 6 cm. Saucer D. 12 cm.   Derby Museum & Art Gallery (34)

82.   TEA BOWL, COFFEE CUP AND SAUCER   *c.*1775-80

Of standard Derby shape; the cup with a simple loop handle.

Painted in enamel colours with rural landscapes in puce in the centre of the saucer, the interior of the coffee cup and tea bowl. Set within a chain border, a foliate leaf motif, set between two chain borders, with the rim of each piece outlined with a gilt dentil border.

Painter possibly Zachariah Boreman.

Mark: Crown, crossed batons, six dots and 'D' in puce enamel.

1 (Gilder's mark – Thos Soar) on all three pieces.

Bowl H. 5 cm. Cup H. 6.7 cm. Saucer D. 12.5 cm.
Derby Museum & Art Gallery (187)

See: Fig.50 for reference to Boreman.

Lit: Bradley, 1978, *op. cit.,* Pl.243 for similar style decoration.

Graham & Oxley, 1981, *op. cit.,* Pl.33 for similar shape and style of decoration.

83. COFFEE CUP AND SAUCER   *c.*1785–90

Cup of ogee shape with entwined loop handle. Saucer cinquefoil shape with shallow moulded ribs radiating from the centre and a shallow well into which the cup fits.

The cup painted in naturalistic enamel colours with fruit and flowers, and sliced fruit, roses and other flowers on the saucer. The terminals on the handle of the cup picked out in turquoise and the rim of the cup and saucer outlined in gilt.

Probably painted by William Billingsley.

Mark: Crown, crossed batons, six dots and 'D' in puce. Impressed 'C' or 'G', and '2' (Gilder's mark – Joseph Staples).

Cup H. 7 cm. Saucer D. 13.5 cm.

Derby Museum & Art Gallery (458-1-1987)

Prov: Major G.N. Dawnay.

Lit: Twitchett, 1980, *op. cit.,* Col.Pl.21.

Cup of truncated cone-shape with handle moulded in the form of intertwined twigs. The saucer with a deep well into which the cup fits and a wide flange.

Painted on the outside of the cup and on the flange of the saucer with rural landscapes in reserved panels on a mazarine-blue ground and *oeil de pedrix*, a gilt dentil border round the inside rim of the cup and the handle picked out in gilt.

Christie's *Sale Catalogue* 7 May, 1782, lists:- 'One pair superbly elegant French-shape cups and saucers Enamel'd in compartments with figures, fine ultramarine blue ground richly finish'd with chased and burnished gold... Lady Weymouth', an entry which refers to this model.

Probably painted by Zachariah Boreman.

Mark: Incised script 'N' and Anchor in gilt on the cup. Incised script 'N' on the saucer.

Cup H. 9.8 cm., Saucer D. 15.6 cm.

Derby Museum & Art Gallery (517-4-1961)

See: Fig.50 for reference to Boreman.

Victoria & Albert Museum (C.267-1935) for similar shape with different decoration.

Lit: Rackham, 1923, *op. cit.,* No.67, Pl.18.

Nightingale, 1881, *op.cit.,* p.71.

Gilhespy, 1965, *op. cit.,* Pl.84.

Twitchett, 1980, *op. cit.,* Pls.114 & 142 for similar shape.

85. TEA BOWL AND SAUCER *c.*1770

The tea bowl painted with pendant floral festoons loosely attached to the scroll-shaped puce and gilt lozenge-shaped border, with a floral bouquet on the inside and a gilt dentil border round the rim. Matching decoration painted on the saucer with a floral spray in the centre and a gilt line round the edge.

Pattern derived from Meissen.

Mark: Crown over 'D' on the bowl. No mark on the saucer.

Bowl H. 5 cm. Saucer D. 13 cm.   Derby Museum & Art Gallery (182)

86. TEA BOWL AND SAUCER *c.*1775

The tea bowl painted with festoons of floral swags painted in monochrome green, suspended from alternating gilt bows and loops, and set below a band of interlinked scrolls and stylised palmettes, two single flowers on the inside and a gilt dentil border round the rim. The saucer painted with a matching decoration.

Mark: Crown entwined with 'D' in gold on the bowl. Crown over 'D' in blue, on the saucer.

Bowl H. 5 cm. Saucer D. 12.5 cm.

Derby Museum & Art Gallery (67)

87. CUP AND SAUCER *c.*1780

Cup of elongated shape with slightly everted rim, a small foot rim and a silver-shaped scroll handle. Saucer of standard Derby shape. The cup painted with three irregular-shaped panels with relief moulding outlined in gilt surrounding a floral spray and scattered single flowers, with the remaining areas painted a distinctive blue, a gilt dentil border round the rim and a gilt line round the foot rim, and the edge of the handle outlined in gilt. The saucer painted with matching decoration.

Mark: Crown over 'D' in blue.

Cup H. 8 cm. Saucer D. 13 cm.　　　Derby Museum & Art Gallery (265)

See: British Museum, 1936, (7-15-115 Paget Collection) for similar cup and saucer.

Lit: Gilhespy, 1965, *op. cit.,* Pl.68 for squat cup with similar shaped handle and similar style decoration.

88. CHOCOLATE CUP AND STAND (cover missing)　　*c.*1775

Cup with slightly everted rim and low spreading foot rim with two loop handles with moulded thumb rests and 'kick' terminals. The saucer with raised *trembleuse* ring in the centre into which the cup fits. Painted with pink and claret stripes, imitating silk ribbons, alternating with garlands of flowers in monotone green, a gilt dentil border round the rim of the cup and saucer and the *trembleuse* ring on the saucer and the handles of the cup outlined in gilt.

Mark: Entwined Anchor and 'D' in gilt. Ground foot rim.

Cup H. 7.5 cm. Saucer D. 14 cm.　　　Derby Museum & Art Gallery (57)

Lit: Rackham, 1923, *op. cit.,* Pl.24, No.71 for Chelsea example.

The can of cylindrical form with loop handle and a deep shaped saucer with a wide flange.

Painted in enamel colours with, on the can two bluetits perched on an arrangement of grapes, peaches and white currants set on a slab, enclosed by a gilt ropework border, the sides decorated with reserves containing bands of roses set on a pale pink ground, and inside the can a gilt lily-of-the-valley motif border and the handle decorated with butterfly gilding. The saucer decorated with alternate oblong and irregular shaped reserves containing roses painted in naturalistic colours outlined in gilt and set on a pale pink ground with a similar gilt lily-of-the-valley motif border round the well-head.

Fruit panel probably painted by George Complin; roses probably painted by William Billingsley.

Mark: Crown, crossed batons, and 'D', and '221' painted in blue enamel. 'L' impressed on the can. 'O' impressed on the saucer. 'V' for the gilder – Jno. Yates.

Cup H. 6.2 cm. Saucer D. 13.3 cm

Derby Museum & Art Gallery (269-1981)

Note: Pattern No. 236 in the Derby Pattern Book 'Fruit with Birds by Complin'. The source of the decoration is taken from Jean Pillement, 1760, *The Ladies Amusement,* London.

Lit: Cook, 1948, *The Life and Work of Robert Hancock,* London. Item No.13.

Bradley, 1978, *op. cit.,* Pl.251 & Col.Pl. advertisement at end.

Jackson, 1987, *The Doris Wheatley Collection of Derby Porcelain,* Dewsbury, W.Yorkshire. Item No.7, for similar shape and style of decoration.

Hoyte, 1987 *A Review of Derby Porcelain. Ceramics,* Vol.VI, November/December, Pl.5.

Lit: Berthoud, 1982, *op. cit.,* Pl.125 for matching tea bowl.

90. CREAMER   *c.*1775

Shallow jug, moulded with shallow spiral flutes shanked from right to left, with a small sparrow-beak lip and wish-bone handle.

Painted with a very narrow dark blue border with gilt dentil edge to the outer rim. Below, a further and slightly wider border in dark blue overlaid with gilt flower heads and the acanthus fronds and the handle outlined in dark blue.

Pattern No. 66.

Mark: 66 in puce. 4 (Gilder – Wm. Yates), 5 (Gilder – Jno. Yates).

H. 7 cm.   Derby Museum & Art Gallery (186)

91. CREAMER

 *c.*1790

Of baluster form, with wide flaring lip and rim drawn out to form a plain loop handle with scroll terminal, set on a low spreading foot.

Painted in enamel colours with a floral chain round the neck and scattered florets in naturalistic colours. The rim of the jug and the handle outlined in gilt and a gilt line round the base.

Mark: Ground-down foot rim.

H. 11.5 cm. Derby Museum & Art Gallery (530)

Lit: Bradley, 1978, *op. cit.,* Pl.263 for similar shape.

Twitchett, 1980, *op. cit.,* Pls.206 & 215 for similar shapes.

92. COW CREAMER   *c.*1765

Figure of cow modelled in a naturalistic manner standing on a double scalloped shell base which rises in the centre to support the animal, with her mouth open for pouring and her tail curled over her back and terminating on the stopper.

The cow painted in naturalistic enamel colours and the moulded scallops on the base decorated in puce enamel and the rim outlined in gilt.

The idea is based on a silver example, first occuring in England in 1753. Cow creamers were copied later at King Street, Derby.

Mark: Patch marks.

H. 10.5 cm. L. 16 cm.   Derby Museum & Art Gallery (367-1982)

Lit: Dawson, 1987, *op. cit.,* for example in British Museum, now thought to be Lowestoft.

93. MUG

Of small size with depressed globular body with wide horizontally-grooved cylindrical neck, a wide loop handle moulded with acanthus leaves and terminal kick. Mugs of this shape and style of decoration, were made in different sizes; together with a jug.

Painted with scattered sprays and sprigs of garden flowers below a shaped 'Smith's' blue border edged with scrolls in gilding. The neck similarly painted with flowers below a blue line border.

Painted in the manner of Edward Withers.

Mark: 'D' intertwined with Anchor, in gilt.

H. 13 cm.   Derby Museum & Art Gallery (76)

See: Victoria & Albert Museum (Schr. 1.444) for similar example.

Lit: Hurlbutt, 1925, *op. cit.,* Pl.9 for matching jug.

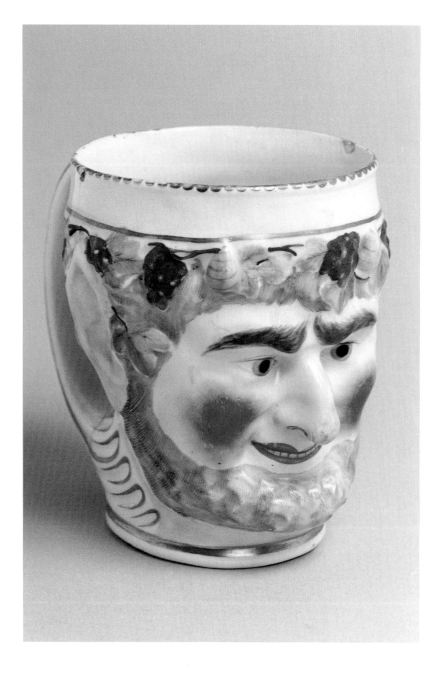

Lit: Gilhespy, 1965, *op. cit.,* Pl.X, for another Bacchante drinking mug.

Barrett & Thorpe, 1971, *op. cit.,* Pl.114.

94. MUG   *c.*1780-85

Drinking mug with a Bacchante mask, modelled with satyr-like features with a broad, flat plain handle.

Christie's Sale Catalogue 17-20 April, 1780 lists: 'Pair of Neptune Heads drinking cups'.

Painted in naturalistic colours.

Mark: Crown over 'D' in blue.

H. 10 cm.   Derby Museum & Art Gallery (275)

95. MUG

Of large cylindrical form, with two moulded bands round the top part of the mug and a flat D-shaped handle, divided at the base terminal, for added strength.

Painted with a band of interlaced ovals and dots above a gold line interwoven with a wavy line with stylised gold leaves. A gilt dentil border round the rim and on the inside, a dot and wavy line border, the handle decorated with a chain of husks and the edge outlined in gilt.

This is an example of Pattern No.53, in the British Museum Derby Pattern Book (Paget Collection Vol.1).

In Sales Ledger Vol.3, 1791, also in the British Museum, William Bemrose Papers, mugs of this size are described as 'Quart toast mugs'.

Mark: Crown, crossed batons, six dots and 'D'.

H. 12.6 cm. D. 12.5 cm.   Private Collection

See: Victoria & Albert Museum (C.244-1922) for a mug of similar shape, marked 'DK' in monogram, surmounted by Crown, crossed batons, six dots, in purple. (Duesbury & Kean 1795-7).

Lit: Bradley, 1978, *op. cit.,* Pl.249 for cup and saucer decorated in a similar style in the City of Bristol Museum & Art Gallery (N 4031a), where it is suggested that it had possibly been made as a replacement for an Anstice, Horton and Rose service.

Hoyte, 1987, *Splendour on Display. The Antique Dealer and Collectors Guide,* March. Fig.3, describing these large mugs as 'Porter mugs'.

Confiture set consisting of two cup-shaped pots with low domed covers surmounted by onion finials, fixed to a shaped tray stand, with up-turned wavy edge.

In the centre of the tray, in an oval reserve on a green ground, a spray of roses painted in naturalistic enamel colours, surrounded by a gilt line; a chain of roses round the up-turned edge of the tray, with similar style decoration round the pots and covers, with a gilt dentil border round the edge of the tray, the rim of the pots and the edge of the covers with the 'onion' finials painted gold.

Probably painted by William Billingsley.

Pattern No. 185.

Mark: Crown, crossed batons, six dots and 'D' in purple. '2' (Gilder's mark – Joseph Staples).

Pots H. 9 cm. Tray L. 25 cm. w. 18.5 cm.

Derby Museum & Art Gallery (425-1976)

Lit: Gage & Marsh, 1988, *Tobacco Containers & Accessories,* London. Pl.28, p.45 for example of Sèvres *plateau à deux pots de confiture* from the Melbourne Service, *c.*1770.

Botanical Decoration on Porcelain

Flower painting had been an early and popular theme in the decoration of European porcelain, and this developed in the second half of the eighteenth century into the portrayal of single plant or flower specimens, often with the plant name inscribed on the reverse of the porcelain, in a manner which may be termed 'botanical'. The interest in botanical gardens in England had first begun at Oxford, later spreading to Chelsea where the Physic Garden was founded by the Worshipful Society of Apothecaries of London in 1673 for the scientific study of plants. But the management of the garden was allowed to decline and it was not until Dr Hans Sloane bought the Manor of Chelsea in 1712 from Charles Cheyne that matters started to improve, and in 1722 he virtually re-founded the Physic Garden.

Philip Miller was appointed Gardener and, two years later, Isaac Rand was appointed *Praefector Horti* (Director). Miller remained at Chelsea for nearly fifty years and it was during this time that his famous *Dictionary of Gardening*, with one edition illustrated, was published and ran through eight editions during his lifetime. Linnaeus is reputed to have said *'Non erit Lexicon Hortulanorum, sed etiam Botanicorum'*. But it was not until the seventh edition of the *Dictionary* that Miller adopted Linnaeus's botanical classification, and the eighth edition the binomial nomenclature which Linnaeus had first introduced in 1735. Miller was eventually succeeded as Gardener by William Forsyth and, following Rand, William Curtis became *Praefector Horti* and Demonstrator of Plants.

The famous Botanic Gardens at Kew date from 1759, when the Dowager Princess of Wales, Princess Augusta, initiated a botanical garden of about nine acres in her private domain at Kew House. This was then a venture of her own and it was fortunate that both she and the son, George III, who succeeded her, had the help first of the Earl of Bute, a botanist of some distinction and later of Sir Joseph Banks. It was under his direction that Kew Gardens became the leading European scientific institution. Sir Joseph was assisted by William Aiton as Curator, a post he held for 48 years.

In 1763 James Smith, as a young man, purchased Linnaeus's collection of specimens and five years later, founded the Linnaen Society, which still continues to function, recording and classifying new species. Thanks to voyages of exploration and trade, a growing flow of new and exotic plants required classification. Nor was the study purely abstract. Cotton seeds were sent from the Physic Garden to Georgia; Chinese bananas were shipped to Fiji and Samoa; and between 1846 and 1848, 20,000 tea plants were taken from Shanghai to the foothills of the Himalayas under the supervision of Robert Fortune, the then Curator, whilst in 1876, Brazilian rubber plants were sent via Kew, to Sri Lanka (Ceylon) and Malaysia.

The building and extension of fine country houses by the nobility and the new classes of wealthy landowners, in a society noted for ostentatious display, led to competition to develop hothouses and gardens and produce new and rare specimens. The periwinkle, first introduced from Madagascar via the Paris *Jardin des Plantes*, reaching England in 1759, when it was described by Miller and given its Latin name *Vinca rosea* by Linnaeus, was typical of the general search for the exotic.

Specialist nurserymen, florists and seedsmen emerged to serve this market, and increasing numbers of illustrated botanical and horticultural books were published: Elizabeth Blackwell, who lived in Swan Walk, adjacent to the Physic Garden, produced the *Curious Herbal*, and the artist Georg-Dionysius Ehret (who married Miller's sister-in-law) illustrated the work of Dr Trew, *Plantae Selectae*, published in ten parts, from 1750 to 1773. Porcelain manufacturers were thus offered both a market for dessert services designed for the display of rare fruits, and sources for their illustration.

Of the English factories, Chelsea is credited with the first use of a botanical illustration, using engravings from the two first parts of *Plantae Selectae*, for the decoration of porcelain during the Red Anchor period.[1] & [2] This style of decoration probably continued through into the Chelsea-Derby period. William Billingsley's imitation or reproduction of such pieces[3] may be said to be the start of Derby's production of 'botanical' dessert services in the early 1790s. None of the Chelsea pieces bore the plant names inscribed on the reverse, and Derby and Royal Copenhagen (*Flora Danica* Service 1790-1802) were the first two factories to introduce such a practice — which obviously depended on the availability of suitable source books for artists to copy.

The correspondence from Joseph Lygo to William Duesbury II in 1792 provides key documentary evidence of the continuing use of botanical illustration and their sources 'Plant dessert, with ice pails to Lord Wentworth', and 'Nineteen numbers of a Botanical magazine sent to Derby'.[4] It has been established that this letter from Lygo refers to the *Botanical Magazine* published by William Curtis[5] and which became the chief source used by Derby artists when decorating botanical dessert services in the 1790s and early 1800s. This use was almost entirely concentrated on the first nine volumes published between 1787-1795.

William Curtis (1746-99), though to a large extent self-taught, was one of the leading field botanists of his time and in addition to his duties at the Physic Garden, was a skilled nurseryman who established his own botanic garden at Lambeth. He was the author of *Flora Londinensis*, which has been described as 'one of the most beautiful and accurate works on British plants'. After several unprofitable publishing ventures he started the *Botanical Magazine* in February 1787, each monthly issue costing one shilling and having three accurately drawn hand-coloured octavo copper engravings accompanied by descriptive pages giving the Latin and English names of the plants, together with botanical, cultivation and historical details. The title page of the first issue proclaimed: 'The most ornamental foreign plants, cultivated in the open ground, the greenhouse and the stove, will be accurately represented in their natural colours'. Curtis also retained a fondness for English garden flowers and these are well represented in the early volumes.

The delicate line drawings were executed by Sydenham Edwards and James Sowerby, the two leading botanical artists of the time, and both of international standing. Sowerby also did the engraving for the first five volumes, before J. Sansom took over that duty, and the hand-colouring was under the supervision of William Graves.

The *Botanical Magazine* set new standards for what was then a popular mass publication, and was deservedly an immediate success, selling 2,000 or more copies of each issue during Curtis's lifetime. The *Botanical Magazine* has remained in continuous production to this day, being now published as the *Kew Magazine*.[6]

Prints from the early volumes of the *Botanical Magazine* are now much sought after, mounted and framed, for decorative purposes, so that complete volumes appearing on the market are likely to be broken up and the interesting textual pages lost. Surviving prints may not always show the true original colours, as the eighteenth century worked with a restricted palette of sometimes fugitive colours, vulnerable to discolouration and darkening by atmospheric pollution. The colours on Derby porcelain may often be truer to the original than surviving prints. Curtis's *Flower Garden Displayed*,[7] shows 120 plants selected from the years 1787-1807 in the chronological order in which the plants are believed to have been introduced to Britain, with the reproductions taken from the originals at Zurich University, which have escaped atmospheric pollution. Examples of several of these can be found on Derby porcelain, such as the Sweet Pea,[8] and the Mexican Poppy on the dessert plate Fig.106.

References
1. Gardner, 1932, *Sir Hans Sloane's Plants on Chelsea Porcelain* Trans. E.P.C. IV, pp. 22-23. See also Baer & Lack, 1979, Berlin; and Murdoch & Twitchett, 1987, London.
2. Synge-Hutchinson, 1958, *G.D. Ehret's Botanical Designs on Chelsea Porcelain, Connoisseur*, Vol. CXLII, no.572, October, pp. 88-94.
3. Thorpe, 1965 *Some Unusual Derby Plates*, The *Antique Collector* August, pp. 166-168.
4. Gilhespy (1965), *op. cit.*, p.70.
5. Advertisement Buckingham Antiques: Twitchett *Antique Dealer and Collectors Guide*. August & September 1968 see also Twitchett, 1980, *op. cit.*, p.206.
6. Desmond, 1987, *A Celebration of Flowers*.
7. Whittle & Cook, 1981, *Curtis's Flower Garden Displayed*.
8. Twitchett, 1980, *op.cit.*, p.206.

97. DESSERT PLATE *c.*1792–1800

Of standard Derby shape, with thirty-two shallow spiral flutes and slightly serrated edge.

In the centre is a flowering convolvulus and others in bud, painted in blue enamel with green leaves attached to the stalk, and a gilt line round the rim of the plate.

The design has been copied from Curtis's *Botanical Magazine* and is a faithful translation of the original, adapted to the shape of the plate by transposing one bud and adding another.

Pattern No.197.

Mark: Crown, crossed batons, six dots and 'D' in blue. Inscribed on reverse '*Convolvulus Tricolour*/Small Convolvulus' in blue.

D. 23 cm.   Derby Museum & Art Gallery (105-1)

Lit: Curtis's *Botanical Magazine*, 1987, Vol.I, Pl.27.

Murdoch & Twitchett, 1987, *Painters and the Derby China Works*, London. No.61, p.111, Morning Glory, *Ipomoea caerulea*, where it is stated that from the late 1780s, Morning Glory was one of the most frequently exploited flowers and that Curtis's *Botanical Magazine* had been available to the workmen at Derby from 1792.

98. DESSERT PLATE *c.*1770

Of standard Derby shape, with spiral flutes and a serrated rim.

Painted in naturalistic enamel colours with cut fruit, flowers and flying insects, with a gilt dentil border round the rim.

Mark: Gold Anchor and 'D'.

D. 22.5 cm. Derby Museum & Art Gallery (83)

Lit: Thorpe, 1965, *Some Unusual Derby Plates, Billingsley decorated 'Replacements' for Chelsea Pieces. The Antique Collector,* August, pp.166–68.

99. DESSERT PLATE   *c.*1790

Shaped as Fig. 97.

Painted in the centre with a campanula (Scottish bluebell) in naturalistic enamel colours with a gilt chain of stylised laurel leaves round the well-head and a broad yellow border between two gilt lines. The harebell was frequently used as a supporting flower when decorating larger pieces – ice pails and tureens.

Presumably the campanula, as a common wild flower, was drawn from nature as no source for the flower has been found in any of the contemporary botanical magazines.

Pattern No.216.

Mark: Crown, crossed batons, six dots and 'D' in blue. Inscribed on reverse 'Campanula' in blue.

D. 22 cm.   Derby Museum & Art Gallery (98-8)

Lit: Gilhespy, 1951, *op. cit.*, Fig.86.

Twitchett, 1980, *op. cit.*, p.135. Pattern No.232 'Green No.8 but with White Enamel but laid over with Green Gold . . . Centre painted with Group of 3 Roses with two buds, Wardle'.

Twitchett, 1980, *op. cit.*, p.281, states that little is known about this painter.

100. DESSERT PLATE   *c.*1790-95

Shaped as Fig. 97.

Painted in the centre with three fully open roses and two buds in naturalistic enamel colours, with a gilt chain of stylised laurel leaves round the well-head and a broad apple-green border between two gilt lines.

Painted by Wardle.

Pattern No.232.

Mark: Stilt marks.

D. 21 cm.   Derby Museum & Art Gallery (127)

101. DESSERT PLATE *c.*1792

Shaped as Fig. 97.

Painted with four vignettes depicting 'Denbigh', 'Raby Castle', 'Lankarne' and 'Pembroke', the titles written beneath each vignette, with in the centre a floral spray painted in pale blue and puce with gilt leaves. A chain floral border, in matching colours painted round the rim, set between two gilt chains of husks and the rim outlined in gilt. This service is known as the 'Castle Service' and includes different groups of castles on each plate.

The source prints from which these were copied have not yet been identified.

Pattern No. 147.

Mark: Crown, crossed batons over 'D' in purple. Stilt marks.

D. 21.5 cm.   Derby Museum & Art Gallery (234)

Lit: Tapp, 1933, *Gilders Marks on Derby China, Connoisseur* Vol.XCI, No.380, April, Pl.X and pp.234-240. Major Tapp considered that the painting had been done by James Banford. He lists another plate in this service with the marks:- 'V' (Jno.Yates), 11. (Wm Taylor) and impressed 'P' which may possibly denote the type of paste being used.

102. DESSERT PLATE   *c*.1784

Of standard shape with thirty-two shallow spiral flutes and serrated
edge.

Painted with a deep border of alternating pale pink and puce vertical
lines, with the face of a cherub, surrounded by tiny gilt dots and laurel
leaves, tied at the base with lovers' knots, placed in the alternate flutes in
an oval surround. A chain of green husks round the well-head and the
rim outlined in gilt.

Pattern No. 153.

Mark: No. 153 in puce. Impressed 'T'. Stilt marks.

D. 21.5 cm.   Derby Museum & Art Gallery (155)

103. DESSERT PLATE   *c.*1787

Plate of standard Derby shape, moulded with thirty-two shallow spiral flutes round the rim and a serrated edge.

Painted in naturalistic enamel colours with a full-blown rose in the centre of a bouquet made up of *myosotis sylvatica* (wood forget-me-nots) and green leaves, surrounded by a circle of gilt dots. A stylised border made up of gilt pendants and alternate gilt dots and pendants round the centre of the rim, surrounded by a salmon-pink outer border and a gilt line round the edge.

Pattern No.65.

From the Prince of Wales Service.

Probably painted by William Billingsley.

Mark: Crown, crossed batons, six dots over 'D' and '65', in puce. Gilder's mark '4' (Wm. Yates). Stilt marks.

D. 22 cm.   Derby Museum & Art Gallery (603-1979)

Lit: John, 1968, *William Billingsley 1758-1828,* Newport, for another plate in this service.

Murdoch & Twitchett, 1987, *op. cit.,* Pl.17a, p.51 for another plate with slightly different border pattern.

104. DESSERT PLATE *c.1770-75*

Plate moulded with a slightly up-turned rim and six indentations forming a wavy rim.

Painted in naturalistic enamel colours, with a small bouquet of flowers in the centre and swags of flowers hanging in the well of the plate, suspended from gilt scrolls, with a shaped turquoise blue border round the rim, set between gilt rococo scrolls and gilt lines, with a gilt dentil border round the edge of the plate.

Mark: Crown over 'D' in blue, and incised 'N'.

D. 21 cm.   Derby Museum & Art Gallery (645-1983)

See: Victoria & Albert Museum (C.1023-1924) for similar shape, but different decoration.

Lit: John, 1968, *op. cit.,* Pl.30(4).

Spero, 1970, *op. cit.,* p.190 for similar shape.

Adams, 1987, *op. cit.,* Pl.125 for cup with similar decoration.

105.   DESSERT PLATE   *c.*1790-95

Plate shaped as No. 101.

Painted in naturalistic enamel colours with a *Campanula speculum* (Venus's Looking Glass) filling the centre of the plate, with a stylised gilt lily-of-the-valley motif border round the rim and the serrated edge outlined in gilt. A very similar, closely copied, example of this flower has been recorded on a dessert plate, Pattern No. 197.

Pattern No. 115.

Mark: Crown, crossed batons and 'D' in blue.

Gilder's mark '18' (John Moscrop) in blue.

Inscribed on the reverse *Campanula speculum*/Venus's Looking Glass, in blue.

D. 23 cm.   Derby Museum & Art Gallery (113-5)

See: Derby Museum (113) for other plates in this service, painted with different botanical flowers.

Fig. 89 for similar lily-of-the-valley border decoration. Fig. 97 for reference to Curtis's *Botanical Magazine*.

Lit: Curtis's *Botanical Magazine,* 1789, November, Vol. 3, Pl. 102.

John, 1968, *op. cit.,* Pl. 14a, for 'botanical' rose.

See: Derby Museum (116) for other plates in this service.

Lit: Curtis's *Botanical Magazine*, 1793, October, Vol.7, Pl.243, where flower has been drawn straight. Here the Derby painter has adapted the design to fit the shape of the plate.

Twitchett, 1980, *op. cit.,* Pl.189, showing the work of a different artist *c.*1800.

Plate shaped as Fig.101.

Painted in naturalistic enamel colours with an *Argemone Mexicana* (Prickly Poppy) filling the centre of the plate, with a continuous floral border set on a dark orange band, round the rim of the plate and the serrated edge outlined in gilt.

Mark: Crown, crossed batons and 'D' in blue.

Inscribed on the reverse *Argemone Mexicana*/Prickly Poppy, in blue.

D. 23.5 cm.
Derby Museum & Art Gallery (116-3)

107 DESSERT PLATE   *c.*1775

Circular plate with a wide rim and deep well centre.

Painted in enamel colours with the decoration divided into ten equal
segments with alternate stylised flower heads on an orange background
and three sprays of flowers and two Chinese figures filling the remaining
five sections, a double circular red line terminating the segments with a
stylised red flower head in the centre and a red wavy line round the rim.

D. 20.5 cm.   Derby Museum & Art Gallery (404-4-59)

Circular saucer-type stand, with the sides of the stand rising steeply, direct from a shallow foot rim.

Painted with, in the centre, a stylised representation of trophies of war, surrounded by a chain of stylised laurel leaves and, on a mazarine-blue ground, decorated with *oeil de pedrix* in gilt, two medallion portraits, on a brown ground, set in gilt frames and alternating with two reserves with war trophies, set in a frame of laurel leaves and all clasped to a pendant chain of stylised laurel leaves outlined in gilt.

Mark: Crown entwined with Anchor and 5 in gold. (Gilder Jno. Yates)

D. 17.8 cm.   Derby Museum & Art Gallery (1408)

See: Victoria & Albert Museum (C.285-1922) for tall jar, cover and stand, painted with similar style of decoration marked Crown over 'D' in gold.

Lit: Barrett & Thorpe, 1971, *op. cit.,* Pl.106.

109.   DESSERT PLATE   *c.*1797–1800

Shaped as Fig. 103.

Painted in naturalistic enamel colours with a distant view of Canterbury
Cathedral, set in the valley of the river Stour, surrounded by a square gilt
dog-tooth frame with a similar style border round the well head and a
green outer border, set between gilt lines.

Probably painted by George Robertson.

Pattern No. 314.

Mark: Crown, crossed batons over 'D' in blue. '314' Stilt marks.

Painted on the reverse, 'View of Canterbury from Harble-down'.

D. 22 cm.   Derby Museum & Art Gallery (114)

Prov: Henry Evans Collection.

Exh: Fine Arts Exhibition, Derby,
1877. No.157.

See: Victoria & Albert Museum
(C.291-1940) for similar style with a
shipping scene in the centre.

View copied from one of the many
engravings of this well-known view.

Lit: Murdoch & Twitchett, 1987, *op.
cit.,* p.93 state that Robertson arrived in
Derby, from Argyll, in 1797 at the age
of 20.

110.   LOBED SAUCER DISH   *c.*1775

Saucer dish with twelve flutes and a wavy edge.

Painted in the centre with grey monochrome urn decorated with a polychrome garland of flowers, set in the centre, surrounded by a blue line entwined with gilt laurel leaves, a Smith's blue border round the outer edge, decorated with gilt palmettes and gilt tooled florets, with a pendant chain of green laurel leaves hanging from the alternate florets, and scattered trophies of war.

Mark: Entwined Gold Anchor and 'D'. Ground foot rim.

D. 22 cm.   Derby Museum & Art Gallery (79)

Lit: Rackham, 1923, *op. cit.*, Pl.29, No.163 for plate with similar style decoration, but different shaped urn.

Barrett & Thorpe, 1971, *op. cit.*, Pl.105.

111.   DESSERT DISH   *c.1775*

Lozenge shape, with fluted flared sides giving an irregular scalloped edge.

Painted in the centre, in naturalistic enamel colours, with a rose and other flowers in a floral bouquet, surrounded by a broad turquoise band with scalloped borders outlined in gilt with scattered floral sprays around the rim and a gilt dentil border round the edge.

Mark: Entwined Gold Anchor and 'D' in gilt. Stilt marks. Ground foot rim.

L. 30 cm. w. 23.5 cm.   Derby Museum & Art Gallery (81)

112. DESSERT DISH *c*.1775

Lozenge shape, with fluted flared sides giving irregular scalloped edge.

Painted with scattered floral sprays and festoons of floral swags, painted in monochrome green, suspended from gilt bows and loops and a gilt dentil border round the edge.

Mark: Entwined Gold Anchor and 'D' in gilt. Stilt marks. Ground foot rim.

L. 4 cm., w. 19 cm. Derby Museum & Art Gallery (53)

See: Fig.86 for similar style of decoration.

113. OVAL DISH   *c.1770*

Navette shaped with fluted flared sides giving an irregular scalloped edge.

Painted in the centre with a stylised urn, decorated with garlands of flowers, surrounded by scattered florets painted at irregular intervals, with twelve-part segments of circles painted in rose pink placed around the rim forming an outer border and each decorated in the centre with a stylised ceremonial axe-head suspended from the rim on turquoise ribbons all joined together by a pendant chain of claret coloured husks, with gilt dots surrounding the segments and a gilt dentil border round the edge.

Mark: Gold Anchor.

L. 23 cm. w. 17 cm.   Derby Museum & Art Gallery (1548)

See: Victoria & Albert Museum (C.334-1922) for a tureen, cover and ladle, decorated in a similar manner, forming part of the set.

114. BASKET

Of rectangular shape with raised sides and shaped rim, with raised cut-out terminals at both ends. Moulded on the outside with basket-weave moulding and rococo scroll work round the handles.

Painted in the centre in naturalistic enamel colours with a bunch of grapes on a stalk with leaves still attached, and scattered butterflies and insects, with four medallion heads painted in profile on a brown background, set in the four cardinal points and framed in a chain of laurel, looped and suspended from gilt rosettes, a gilt dentil border round the edge and the rococo handles picked out in turquoise.

Part of the Egerton Service.

Mark: Patch marks. Entwined Anchor and 'D' in gold.

L. 22.5 cm.   Derby Museum & Art Gallery (216)

See: Derby Museum (87) for plates D.21.5 cm. in this service and dishes (241-582, 1892) of similar shape.

Victoria & Albert Museum (C.355-1922) for similar shape with stand, decorated with an urn in the centre of the dish.

Lit: Gilhespy, 1951, *op. cit.,* Fig.113.

115. DISH   *c.*1780

Of square form with canted sides formed by twelve scallop flutes, and
wavy rim.

Painted in the centre with a rose and other garden flowers in naturalistic
enamel colours and surrounded by a circular blue line with scattered
flowers and a chain of husks painted in puce suspended from gilt rings
attached to a mazarine-blue band decorated with stylised gilt florets, set
between gilt lines and a gilt border.

Probably painted by William Billingsley.

D. 18 cm.   Derby Museum & Art Gallery (278)

116.   TUREEN, COVER AND STAND   *c.*1795

Of 'Adam' silver shape with pointed loop handles rising above the rim of the tureen, set on a raised pedestal foot. A domed cover with cut-out for a ladle and surmounted by a loop handle formed by two stalks knotted in the centre and terminating in leaf moulding. A *navette*-shaped stand with flat base.

White reserves on each piece painted with specimen botanical flowers surrounded by a stylised leaf chain and an iron-red border set between gilt lines with the handles of the tureen and the cover outlined in gilt.

Pattern No.313.

Probably painted by John Brewer.

Mark: Crown, crossed batons, six dots & 'D' and 313, in blue enamel. Inscribed 'Cineraria Amelloides — Cape Aster' and 'Mimosa Verticillata — Whorl'd leav'd Mimosa' in blue, on the tureen.

See: Derby Museum (830) for similar shape, marked with the 'Ting' or 'Potter's Stool', painted in puce.

'Alyssum Deltoideum – Purple Alyssum' in grey on the cover.

L. 22 cm.   Derby Museum & Art Gallery (599)

Blue and White

From the early days, after Duesbury had become manager, blue and white decorated porcelain must have been made at Derby, something that is confirmed by a tea bowl and a pair of coffee cups in the Derby Museum & Art Gallery (1168-1,2,3), which are thought to date from 1756-58, and a ladle[1] and chamber candlestick[2] both painted in a similar style of decoration, in a soft pale blue colour and to belong to this early period. But few other pieces of a pre-1760 date have survived and this may have been due to the type of paste being used, as mentioned in the chapter on tea wares.

The wide range of the blue colour on Derby porcelain from the soft-toned blue of the early period through to a very dark violet-blue has caused people to doubt the Derby attribution. The colour variation may have been caused by the cobalt being used, particularly during the early years. Due to the Seven Years War (1756-63) the cobalt ore mined in Saxony was expensive and incurred heavy import dues. The Duke of Saxony tried to forbid the export of natural cobalt, which necessitated a search for alternative sources. In 1755 the Royal Society of Arts had given an award to Francis Beauchamp[3] for the discovery of rich deposits from a mine near Truro, but considerable difficulty was still experienced in the manufacture of zaffre (calcinated cobalt ore fritted with sand) and smalt (zaffre fused with potassium carbonate to form a dark blue glass) due to lack of technical knowledge. Much of it had to be imported and in the Duesbury manuscripts (508)[4] there is a reference stating that Hull is the best market for powder blue. Also there is a reference to a bill dated 28 March, 1795[5] from Messrs Grace & Freeman, Indigo Makers, Aldermanbury, Postern, London for smalts.

Jewitt[6] writing in 1878, lists several articles decorated in blue and white which were sent from Derby to London in 1765: 'Box No.11 contained twelve round fourth-sized, open-worked Baskets and the list included blue fluted boats, blue strawberry pots, and blue guglets and basins to ditto',[7] thus proving that articles decorated in blue and white were made in a wide variety of shapes. But it will be noted that tea and coffee services are not included in this list even though they were certainly being made at this date. There are no 'melon' shaped teapots similar to the ones illustrated in Bradley,[8] but several early conical shaped pots have survived and this may have been due to the fact that they were used for hot chocolate, made and drunk at a lower temperature than coffee, and so were not submitted to the test of boiling water.

During this early period, most of the wares have 'patch marks' on the base (Figs. 121 & 122) and as with the polychrome wares, many of the foot rims needed to be ground down to produce a flat surface. One of the characteristics noted on Derby blue and white, on both painted and transfer-printed wares, is the tendency for the design to blur in the glaze and this may have been due to the fact that after the cobalt design was applied to the biscuit, it was not given a

slight hardening-on or drying out to help fix the design.

Following the amalgamation with Chelsea the Crown over 'D' mark is sometimes used; also the script 'N' either incised or painted is found, particularly on asparagus servers (Fig.117) but no satisfactory reason for the 'N' has been put forward. Only two dated pieces of Derby blue and white have been recorded. One, the salt in the Castle Museum, Norwich (48-941), inscribed on the base 'M x S 1772',[9] which was for many years thought of as Lowestoft; and on the underside of a perforated bowl cover is written in underglazed blue 'August 1762'[10] which is in the Godden Reference Collection. These bowls with perforated covers are usually referred to as 'chestnut bowls', but if chestnuts were to be eaten hot, the perforation in the cover would tend to cool them rather than help to retain the heat. However there was on display at the 1989 Grosvenor House Antiques Fair, a large bowl with a solid cover and it would seem that this would better fit the description of a chestnut bowl, and that those with a perforated cover would be more suitable for fresh fruit such as strawberries. Unfortunately most of these bowls and covers have become separated from their stands, but since the heavy bowls have no handles, it stands to reason that they would have been placed on a stand, so that they could have been passed around at the table.

Except for the vase decorated in sponged powder blue and another vase of a slightly similar shape, almost all the wares decorated in blue and white were made not for decoration but for use: in addition to those that could be used on the table, there were inkwells for writing; patch stands for the dressing table; feeding cups for the sick and guglets for holding water (which 'guggled' when tilted for pouring), with a matching bowl for washing, and that most essential item the chamber candlestick. Few of these objects have survived the passage of time.

When surveying the range of wares of this early period, one cannot help being surprised by the number of different shapes of sauceboats that were produced, ranging from small butter boats to ones 23.5 cm in length. Also the variety of shapes in production must have been greater than any of the other rival porcelain factories. The visual magnificence of the centrepieces formed by a group of scallop shells, set on a shell encrusted base, and surmounted by a kingfisher perched on a branch[11] can only be surpassed by some that were produced at the Bow factory.

It was thought for many years that little blue and white porcelain was made at Derby, but after the 'shock' of seeing the display included in the exhibition held at Morley College, London, in November 1976, this could no longer be accepted as fact. Only fifteen years earlier, when Gilhespy published his book *Derby Porcelain*[12] he referred to the difficulty of having to compose a chapter on such a restricted field. It was also at one time suggested that Duesbury did not like this form of decoration, but even in the year following his death, the entries in the account book quoted by Barrett and Thorpe,[13] covering the period April 1787-

January 1788, the list includes: '6 Egg cups, 16 Egg spoons, 6 Hartichoke cups, Asparagus servers (Fig.117), 12 small Patty pans, 1 pair Potting pots, 1 pair Butter Tubs, covers and stands, 2 large & 4 small Pickle leaves and 2 small Vine leaves, 3 Pint & 3 Half-pint Basins, a Toy cream jug and 2 Saucers; also 2 small Jugs and a slop basin enamelled in fine blue and white', which in the case of the jug cost 12s.0d each, the same price as the pair of butter tubs, covers and stands.

It is always difficult to convert current costs into present day prices, and when Dr Johnson visited Derby in 1777 and went to see the china manufactory there, he is reported by Boswell to have observed 'it was too dear; for that he could have vessels of silver, of the same size, as cheap as what were made here of porcelain'. The footnote to the sale held on the 9 May 1783 added by Nightingale that 'Dr Johnson . . . bought several lots including one consisting of six scallop shells, 6 asparagus servers and 6 artichoke cups, blue and white for 7s.0d'[14] is incorrect. As pointed out by Mallet[15] this refers not to Samuel Johnson but, most probably, to Dr Alexander Johnson who was interested in the manufacture of porcelain and was known to Duesbury II. Other lots included 'One pair of butter tubs, covers and stands, enamel'd blue Chantilly pattern 6s.0d; Six French shape cups and saucers, enamel'd fine blue and white 14s. 0d; and One pair of potting pots, blue and white landscape pattern 4s. 6d.'

It will be noted that none of these lists give any indication of whether the items were painted or transfer-printed, a process which had been carried out at Derby since the mid-1760s. An agreement signed in 1764, between Duesbury, Heath and Richard Holdship, one of the original partners of the Worcester Porcelain Company, stated 'that Holdship agreed to sell his "secret process" for making china, using soapstone, and to teach enamelling "in blew" and blue printing'. But in spite of this very few transfer-printed designs can be considered as exclusive to Derby, and the occasional use of printed designs on wares made both at the China Factory and the Cockpit Hill Pot Works, adds to the problem of attribution. It must be remembered that John Heath, the Derby banker, who became sole proprietor in 1770 of the Pot Works, later taking his brother Christopher into Partnership, also had a financial hold over the China Factory.

Probably one of the last transfer-printed patterns produced at Derby was the 'Nankin' pattern (Fig.118) and it must be admitted that even with the addition of gilding, it is of limited appeal, but a large coffee pot was sold at auction 7 May, 1782 for 5s.0d. and a complete set of china, Nankin pattern, was sold three years earlier for £1. 8s.0d.[16]

The demand for blue and white decoration must have continued, because in the Lygo correspondence,[17] against the date 1796, is a note 'Blue and white basins' and against the year 1791, 'Blue-and-white service for Mr. Frankley. Not determined upon a border for the "blue under the glaze" for Mr. Digby's plate — in the meantime

Taylor will be going on with the painting in the middle'. This was probably the same decorator as mentioned by Samuel Keys when he set down his recollections in 1837, which were published by Wallis and Bemrose, 1870,[18] Keys had been apprenticed to Duesbury in 1785 and he stated 'When I first went to work, Mr. Taylor painted only blue under the glaze on biscuit. That failed, and he asked permission to paint on the glaze, and paid his foot-ale for it'. Twitchett[19] quotes Jewitt stating that in 1784, Taylor had decorated the centre of a service of plates for a Mr Digby, and goes on to state that he became a gilder and was given the number 11.

It is most likely that during the earlier years, any of the artist/decorators working at Derby, would have been able to paint in underglaze blue, but their work remains anonymous and only the name of Taylor has come down to us.

1. Bradley, 1978, *op. cit.*, No.206, p.126.
2. Watney, 1973, *op. cit.*, Pl.63.B.
3. Watney, 1973, *op. it.*, *p.3.*
4. *Bradley, 1978, op. cit., p.96.*
5. Barrett & Thorpe, 1971, *op. cit.*, p.156.
6. Jewitt, 1878, *op. cit.*, p.68-9.
7. Bradley, 1978, *op. cit.*, p.96.
8. Bradley, 1978, *op. cit.*, No.181, p.116.
9. Watney, 1973, *op. cit.*, Pl.65 A.
10. Godden, 1985, *Some Documentary Porcelain, Ceramics* I, p.89.
11. Watney, 1973, *op. cit.*, Pl.69a.
12. Gilhespy, 1961, *op. cit.*, p.102.
13. Barrett & Thorpe, 1971, *op.cit.*, pps.154-5.
14. Nightingale, 1881 (reprint 1973), *op. cit.*, pps. 73, 76 & 77.
15. Mallet, 1985, *Johnson and Porcelain Manufacture* Journal of the Royal Society of Arts, Vol. CXXXIII, August, p.
16. Nightingale, 1881 (reprint 1973), *op.cit.*, pps. 55 & 70.
17. Gilhespy, 1961, *op.cit.*, pps.76 & 75.
18. Wallis & Bemrose, 1870, *The Pottery & Porcelain of Derbyshire* p.12.
19. Twitchett, 1980, *op. cit.*, p.276.

117. ASPARAGUS SERVER   *c.*1778-82

Tapering fan-shaped body with upright sides with undulating rim.

Painted in underglaze blue with a Chinese pagoda beside an estuary.

Mark: 'N' in underglaze blue.

L. 7.5 cm.   Derby Museum & Art Gallery (56-4)

Lit: Spero, 1970, *op.cit.,* p.205 for similar shape.

Bradley, 1978, *op.cit.,* Pl.190 for similar shape.

118. TEA BOWL AND SAUCER   *c.*1775-80

Transfer-print in dark underglaze blue with an oriental landscape and diaper cell border round the rim of the saucer and the inside of the bowl. Traces of gilding round the foot rim and the inside rim of the bowl and the rim of the saucer. Known as 'Nankin' pattern.

Bowl H. 4.5 cm.

Saucer D. 12.5 cm.   Derby Museum & Art Gallery (568-4-62)

Exh: Morley College, London. 1976.

Lit: Bradley, 1978, *op.cit.,* Pl.157.

119. SALT   *c.*1775

Shallow cup-form with applied *schneeballen* (may flowers), with everted
rim and standing on three shaped feet.

Painted in underglaze blue with a dentil border round the rim and the
cartouche moulding round the feet outlined in blue.

H. 4.8 cm. D. 8.2 cm.   Derby Museum & Art Gallery (719-1983)

See: Victoria & Albert Museum
(C.2001-1901) for similar shape with
lion paw feet, painted in turquoise
enamel.

Lit: Bradley, 1978, *op.cit.,* Pl.80 for
similar shape.

Gabszewicz & Freeman, 1982, *op.cit.,*
Pl.43, for Bow example of similar
shape with applied double-prunus
flower sprays.

120. BUTTER BOAT   *c.*1760

Reeded body moulded with flowers and fruiting vine, with a silver-
shape scroll handle. Decoration after a salt-glaze mould.

Painted in underglaze blue on the moulded decoration on the outside and
a stylised flower and cell diaper border round the inside and a scroll
decoration on the handle.

L. 11 cm.   Derby Museum & Art Gallery (45-1978)

Lit: Spero, 1970, *op.cit.,* p.195.

Bradley, 1978, *op.cit.,* Pl.193 for
similar shape.

121. SWEETMEAT STAND AND BASE   *c.1758-60*

Seven open scallop shells arranged in three tiers around a central column, encrusted with shells and seaweed and rocks. The cylindrical base encrusted with murex, whelks, cowries and other shells, probably all modelled from nature.

Painted in underglaze blue with stylised paeonies on each scallop shell and surrounded by a lattice border. The moulding on the shell-encrusted central column and on the cylindrical base picked out in blue.

Mark: Three patch marks on base.

H. 27 cm.   Derby Museum & Art Gallery (330-57)

Note: A similar example, formerly in the T. G. Cannon Collection was sold in the Anderson Galleries, New York, in January 1927, when it was catalogued as Chelsea.

See: Plymouth City Museum for a polychrome example.

Lit: Barrett & Thorpe, 1971, *op. cit.* Pl.27.

122. PIERCED BASKET   *c.*1760

Circular open-work pierced basket with double rope twist handles terminating in flower finials, moulded on the inside, and applied florets at the intersections around the inside of the rim. Part of the flared side wall in one place has partially collapsed in the firing, giving the basket a slightly oval shape.

Painted in underglaze blue with an oriental landscape set in a central reserve and a small cell diaper border round the rim with the handles and the florets picked out in blue.

Mark: Patch marks.

D. (of base) 11 cm. L. 17.5 cm.   Derby Museum & Art Gallery (568-62)

Lit: Spero, 1970, *op.cit.,* p.200 for similar shape.

Barrett & Thorpe, 1971, *op.cit.,* Pl.82.

Watney, 2nd Ed. 1973, *op.cit.,* Pl.64a, for similar shape.

Bradley, 1978, *op.cit.,* Pl.210 for similar decoration.

BIBLIOGRAPHY

Adams, E. 1987, *Chelsea Porcelain*, London.

Adams, E. & Redstone, D. 1981, *Bow Porcelain*, London.

Austin, J.C. 1977, *Chelsea Porcelain at Williamsburg*, Williamsburg, Va.

Barnard, H. 1924, *Chats on Wedgwood Ware*, London.

Baer, W. & Lack, W., 1979, *Pflanzer auf Porzellan*, Berlin.

Barrett, F.A. & Thorpe, A.L. 1971, *Derby Porcelain*, London

Bemrose, W. 1898, *Bow, Chelsea and Derby Porcelain*, Derby

Berthoud, M. 1982, *An Anthology of British Cups*, Wingham, Kent

Blunt, R. (Ed.) 1924, *The Cheyne Book of Chelsea China and Pottery*, London

Bourgeois, E. 1909, *Le Biscuit de Sevre de Dix-huitième siêcle*, Paris.

Bradley, H.G. (Ed.) 1978, *Ceramics of Derbyshire 1750-1975*, Tiverton, Devon

Bradshaw, P. 1981, *Eighteenth Century English Porcelain Figures, 1745-1795*, Woodbridge, Suffolk

Britton, F. 1987, *London Delftware*, Milton Keynes

Chapel, J. & Gore, C. 1985, *The Fine and Decorative Art Collections of Britain and Ireland*, London

Cook, C. 1948, *The Life and Work of Robert Hancock*, London

Desmond, R. 1987, *A Celebration of Flowers*

Gabszewicz A. & Freeman, G. 1982, Bow Porcelain, London

Gage, D. & Marsh, M. 1988, *Tobacco Containers & Accessories*

Gilhespy, F.B. 1951, *Crown Derby Porcelain*, Leigh-on-Sea

———— 1965, (2nd Ed.), *Derby Porcelain*, London

Godden, G.A. 1969, *The Illustrated Guide to Lowestoft Porcelain*, London

———— 1974, *British Porcelain, an Illustrated Guide*, London

Gunnis, R. 1953, *Dictionary of British Sculptors 1660-1851*. London.

Hackenbroch, Y. 1957, *Chelsea and Other English Porcelain, Pottery and Enamel in the Urwin Untermeyer Collection*, Cambridge, Mass.

Haslem, J. 1876 (reprint 1973), *The Old Derby China Factory*, London

Hobson, R.L. 1905, *Catalogue of English Porcelain in the British Museum*, London

Hodgson, Mrs. W. 1906, *How to Identify Old China*, London

Honey, W.B. 1928, *Old English Porcelain*, London

Hurlbutt, F. 1925, *Old Derby Porcelain and its Artist Workmen*, London

Hyam, E. 1926, *The Early Period of Derby Porcelain*, London

Jewitt, Ll. 1878, *The Ceramic Art of Great Britain*, London

John, W.D. 1968, *William Billingsley 1758-1828*, Newport, Mon.

King, W. 1925, *English Porcelain Figures of the Eighteenth Century*, London

The Ladies Amusement, 1750 (reprint 1966), London

Lane, A. 1961, *English Porcelain Figures of the Eighteenth Century*, London

Lippert, C.B. 1987, *Eighteenth-Century English Porcelain in the Collection of the Indianapolis Museum of Art*, Indianapolis, Indiana

Mackenna, F.S. 1951, *Chelsea Porcelain. The Red Anchor Wares*, Leigh-on-Sea

———— 1972, *The F.S. Mackenna Collection of English Porcelain Part 1, Chelsea 1743-1758*, Leigh-on-Sea

Marshall, C.H.R. 1954, *Coloured Worcester Porcelain of the First Period, 1751-1783*, Newport, Mon.

Miller, P. & Berthoud, M. 1985, *An Anthology of British Teapots*, Wingham

Morley-Fletcher, H. 1968, *Investing in Pottery and Porcelain*, London

Murdoch, J. & Twitchett, J. 1987, *Painters and the Derby China Works*, London

Nightingale, J.E. 1881 (reprint 1973), *Contributions towards the History of Early English Porcelain from Contemporary Sources*, Salisbury

Rackham, B. 1928 (revised), *Catalogue of the Schreiber Collection of English Porcelain*, London

———— 1923, *Catalogue of the Herbert Allen Collection of English Porcelain*, London

Rice, D.G. 1983, *Derby Porcelain, the Golden Years 1750-1770*, Newton Abbot, Devon

Sandon, H. 1969, *The Illustrated Guide to Worcester Porcelain, 1751-1793*, London

Savage, G. 1961, *English Pottery and Porcelain*, London

Scott, C.M. & G.R. 1961, *Antique Porcelain Digest*, Bath, Somerset

Smith, S. 1975, *Lowestoft Porcelain in Norwich Castle Museum*, Great Yarmouth

Spero, S. 1970, *The Price Guide to 18th Century English Porcelain*, Woodbridge, Suffolk

Stoner, F. 1955, *Chelsea, Bow and Derby Porcelain Figures*, Newport, Mon.

Tilley, F. 1957, *Teapots and Tea*, Newport, Mon.

Twitchett, J. 1980, *Derby Porcelain*, London

———— 1976, *Royal Crown Derby*, London.

Wallis, A. & Bemrose, W.M., 1870, *The Pottery & Porcelain of Derbyshire*

Walton, P. 1976, *Creamware and other English Pottery at Temple Newsam House, Leeds*, Bradford & London

Watney, B. 1957, *Longton Hall Porcelain*, London

—— 1973 (2nd Ed.), *English Blue & White Porcelain of the 18th Century*, London

Whittle, T. & Cook, C., 1981, *Curtis's Flower Garden Displayed*

PERIODICALS

Anderson, J. 1986, *Two remarkable pieces of Derby Porcelain*, DPIS Newsletter, No.7 December

—— 1987, *Wm. Duesbury, father and son, Men of Industry*, Derby Museum & Art Gallery

Bowles, C. 1786, *New and Enlarged Catalogue*, London

Christie's 1756, 1771, 1773, 1780 and 1782 Sale Catalogue

Clifford, T. 1969, *Derby Biscuit*, Trans. E.C.C., Vol.7, Pt.2.

—— 1978, Some English Ceramic Vases and their Sources Part 1. Trans. E.C.C. Vol.10, Pt.3.

Curtis's Botanical Magazine, 1789, Vol.3, November.

Curtis's Botanical Magazine, 1793, Vol.7, October

Curtis's Botanical Magazine, 1987, Vol.1, October

Dawson, A. 1987, *Eighteenth Century English Porcelain from the British Museum*, The International Ceramics Fair & Seminar London

—— 1988, *The F. Howard Paget Collection* DPIS Newsletter No.11 January

Derby Porcelain International Society, Journal No.1

Trans. E.C.C., *Miscellany*, Vol.5 Pt.4

Gage, D. & Marsh, M. 1988, *Tobacco Containers & Accessories*.

Gardner, B. 1943, *Birds, Beasts and Fishes*, Antique Collector, Jan./Feb.

Gardner, B. 1932, *Sir Hans Sloane's Plants on Chelsea Porcelain*, Trans. E.C.C. IV

Gentleman's Magazine, 1799, 4 October 1800, 29 September

Godden, G.A., 1975, 'Some Documentary Porcelain' *Ceramics* first issue.

Graham, M. & Oxley, J. 1981, *English Porcelain Painters*, Exhibition Catalogue.

Hillis, M. 1985, *The Liverpool Porcelains*, N.C.S., Occasional Paper No.1

Hodgson, Z. 1986, *Fishers or Birdcatchers*, Ceramics, July/August

Honey, W.B., Rackham, B., & Read, H. 1926, *Early Derby Porcelain*, Burlington Magazine, Vol. LXIX, No.CCLXXV, December

Hoyte, A. 1987, *Splendour on Display*, The Antique Dealer and Collectors Guide, March

—— 1987, *A Review of Derby Porcelain*, Ceramics, Vol.VI, Nov./Dec.

Hurlbutt, F. 1933, *Some Vases in the Hurlbutt Collection*, Connoisseur, Vol.XCI, No. 377, January

Jackson, P. 1987, *The Doris Wheatley Collection of Derby Porcelain*, Exhibition Catalogue, Dewsbury, W. Yorkshire

—— 1988, *The Dynamic Brilliance of Derby Porcelain. The First Hundred Years.* Exhibition Catalogue, Brackley, Northants.

Jottrand, M. 1989, *New Thoughts on Tournai Porcelain Sculpture*, The International Ceramics Fair and Seminar

King, W. 1929, 'For the Connoisseur', *English Porcelain at the British Museum. 1. Early Derby*, Country Life, Vol.LXV, January

—— 1938, *The Wallace Elliot Bequest of English Porcelain and Pottery*, British Museum Quarterly, Vol.XII no.3.

MacAlister, Mrs. D. 1929, *The Early Works of Planché and Duesbury*, Trans. E.P.C., No.2

—— 1931, *William Duesbury's London Account Book, 1751-1753*, E.P.C., Monograph, London

Mallet, J.V.G. 1969, *Rococo English Porcelain. A Study in Style*, Apollo, Vol.XC, No.90, August.

—— 1984, *Rococo in English Ceramics*, Exhibition Catalogue V & A

—— 1985, 'Johnson and Porselain Manufacture' Journal of the Royakl Society of Arts, Vol. CXXXIII, August, pp.624-28.

Roth, C. 1989, *Rococo*, DPIS Journal 1

Rowan, P. 1988, *Derby Models Rediscovered*, The Antique Dealer and Collectors Guide, May

Rückert, R. 1965, *Meissener Porzellan 1710-1810*, Exhibition Catalogue Munich

Stoner, F. 1924, *Chelsea Moulds: an Important Discovery*, Connoisseur, Vol.LXIX, No. 273, May

Synge-Hutchinson, P. 1958, *G.D. Ehret's Botanical Designs on Chelsea Porcelain*, Connoisseur, Vol. ? June

Tapp, W.H. 1933, *Gilders Marks on Derby China*, Connoisseur, Vol.XCI, No.380, April

—— 1934, *Zachariah Borman*, Connoisseur Vol.XCIII, January

—— 1934, *Richard Askew*, Connoisseur, Vol. XCIII, June

—— 1939, *Thomas Hughes*, First Enameller of English China, of Clerkenwell. Trans E.C.C., Vol.2, No.6.

Thorpe, A.L. 1965, *Some Unusual Derby Plates, Billingsley Decorated 'Replacements' for Chelsea Pieces,* Antique Collector, August

Towner, D. 1963, *William Greatbach and the Early Wedgwood Ware,* Trans. E.C.C., Vol.5, Pt.4

Twitchett, J. 1987, *Wm. Duesbury. A Man of Achievement,* Ceramics, Vol.V, August

Watney, B. 1980, *Some Parallels and Prototypes in Ceramics,* Trans. E.C.C., Vol.10, Pt.5.

Williams, W. 1973, *Early Derby Porcelain,* Exhibition Catalogue

—— 1975, *Eighteenth Century European White Porcelain.* Burlington House Fair, 1985, Exhibition Catalogue

Williamson, F. 1927, Thew beginnings of Porcelain Manufacture in Derby *Conoisseur,* LXXVII, April.

Index

Actor, 46.
Aesop's Fables, 53, 65, 71.
Arts and Sciences, 87.
Askew, Richard, 12, 18, 96, 104, 105, 106, 116, 133.

Bacchus and Cupid, 87.
Bacchus with Youthful Satyr, 77.
Bacchantes Worshipping a Herm of Pan, 93.
Bacon, John, 75, 85, 86, 95, 96, 102.
Banford, James, 18, 19, 21, 110.
Barton (Gilder), 17.
Belfield, Edward, 14.
Bemrose, William, 12.
Bentley, Thomas, 29, 86.
Billingsley, William, 6, 7, 13, 18, 22, 24, 49, 110, 116, 135, 139, 146, 148, 156, 168.
— Family, 12.
— Mary, 49.
— William, Senior, 13, 14.
Boar, Seated, 31, *33*.
— *Running*, 31.
Boreman, Zachariah, 7, 18, 25, 96, 104, 105, 110, 116, 134, 136.
Boucher, François, 43, 90.
Bouchardon, 96.
Bow Porcelain, 7, 40, 41, 46, 66.
Boy Holding a Posy, 70.
Boy with a Dog, 46.
Bradbury, George (Repairer), 13.
Brewer, John, 12, 18, 19, 169.
Briand, Thomas, 27.
Brocklesbury, 16, 19.
Broughton, Thomas, (Painter), 14.
Bull, Charging, 31, *34*.
Burke, Thomas, 96, 110.
Butler, J., 14.

Canaries, 35.
Catherine, Mr. (Modeller), 10, 22, 24.
Chawner, Rev., 16.
Chaucer, 88.
Chelsea Porcelain Factory, 6, 7, 9, 12, 13, 23, 31, 36, 40, 41, 43, 46, 49, 65, 66, 72, 74, 78, 85, 86, 87, 95, 96, 148, 171.
Chinaman perched on Rocks and a Boy, *45*.
Chinese Boy robbing a Nest, 67.
Chinese Export Ware, 64, 112.
Christ, Figure of, 88.
Christie and Ansell, 85, 95.
Christie, Mr., 10, 21, 29, 86.
Clive, Kitty, 46.
Clark (Gilder), 17.
Cockpit Hill Works, 26, 28.
Coffee, John William (Modeller), 75.
Commedia Dell'Arte, 66, 73.
Complin, George, 18, 20, 116, 139.
Cooper, William (Painter), 13, 14, 17, 119.
Cope and Biddle, 24.
Covent Garden Showroom, 9, 14.

Crested Pheasant Candlestick, 46, *48*.
Crisp, Nicholas, 27, 46, 86.
Cunningham, Mr., 14, 74.
Cupid with a Dog, 92.
Cupid with a Falcon, 91.
Curtis, William, 147, 148, 149, 150.

Dancing Boy, 46.
Deare, John, 14, 74.
'The Deares', 14.
Derby China Works, 9, 11, 12, 13, 15, 16, 20, 22, 23, 26, 29, 75.
DPIS, 6, 112.
Dixon, William (Artist), 116.
Duesbury, Henry, 86.
— James, 16, 25.
— John, 114, 126.
— William I, 6, 9, 10, 11, 12, 13, 14, 15, 16, 23, 26, 29, 31, 44, 46, 49, 50, 52, 65, 74, 86, 95, 172.
— William II, 6, 9, 10, 11, 12, 13, 15, 16, 17, 18, 20, 22, 23, 24, 25, 112, 148.
Duvivier, Fidèle, 49.

East India Company, 23.
Eberlin, J. F., 65, 70, 77.
Edkins, Thomas (Painter), 49.
Ehder, J. G., 58.
Egan, Richard, 13.
— Anne (née Duesbury), 13, 15.
Elements The, 43, 74, 80, 87.
   Air, 87.
   Earth, 87.
   Fire, 87.
   Water (Neptune), 43, 80, 87.

F., Thomas (Painter), 49.
Falconet, E. M., 90.
Filipart, P., 107.
Four Continents (Quarters of the Globe), 74, *78*.
   Asia, 78, *79*.
   America, 78, *79*.
Four Seasons, 74, 77.
   Autumn, 77.
Frost, John (Painter), 13.

Gadsby, William (Mould Maker), 14.
Gardener and Companion, 87.
Garrick, 88.
Gauron, Nicholas, 14, 86.
Giles, James, 14.
Girl on a Horse, 46.
Girl with a Lamb, 46.

Hancock, John, 24.
Hand, William, 14.
Hardenberg. B. F., 75.
Heald, Joseph, 14.
Heath, John, 9, 26, 172.
Heath & Company, 26.
Hercules, 87.
Hill, 'Jockey', 19.
Holdship, Richard, 172.
Homes, 29.
Horace, 88.

Jason and Medea before Artemis, 83.
Jupiter, 81, 82.
Juno, 81, *82*.

Kändler, J. J., 40, 41, 43, 47, 73.
Kauffmann, Angelica, 96, 110.
Kean, Michael, 11, 13, 16, 25.
Keene, David, 14.
Kent, William, 76.
Keys, Samuel (Gilder), 17.
King, Charles, 11, 18, 20, 25.

Lady and Servant, 43, 47.
Lamb, 31, *36*.
Leopard, *37*.
Longden (Gilder), 17, 129.
Locker, William, 29.
Longton Hall, 26, 40, 49, 52.
Lygo, Joseph, 9, 10, 11, 12, 15, 16, 17, 18, 19, 20, 21, 22, 23, 24, 25, 74, 75, 88, 95, 96, 112, 113, 114, 148, 172.

Macaulay, Mrs., 14, 88.
Madonna, 88.
Map Seller, 43.
Mason, Thomas (Repairer), 17, 19, 49.
Marchand, James (Potter), 27.
Meissen (Dresden), 6, 10, 22, 27, 29, 31, 34, 36, 40, 41, 43, 50, 58, 65, 66, 70, 72, 73, 77, 78, 96, 101, 137.
Meyer, Friedrich Elias, 78.
Micali (Dealer), 22.
Milton, 76.
Minerva, 87.
Morgan, Thomas, 14.
Moore, William, 14.
Morlidge, John (Repairer), 13, 14.
Moscrop, John (Gilder), 158.
Muses, The, 87, *94*.
Three Muses with an Urn, *94*.
Musgrove, John, 25.
Musicians, 43.
   Fife and Drum Player, 68.
   Flute Player, 42.
   Man with a Lute, 43.
   Woman with a Drum, 43.

Negro Boy, 69.
Neptune and Amphritite, 88.
Nurnburg, Mr., 21.

Pardoe, William and Alice, 14.
Partridge Tureen, *41*.
Pastoral Group, 90.
Peart, Charles, 75, 88.
Pennington, Robert (Painter), 14.
Philips, Edward (Painter), 14.
Pinxton, 24, 75.
Planché, Andrew, 6, 7, 9, 26, 27, 28, 29, 42.
Porter, John (Painter), 13.
Pug, 46.

Horsley, William, 17.
Horwell, Charles, 74.

Raimondi, Marc Antonio, 94.
Raphael, 94.
Reinicke, 43.
Ridinger, Johann Elias, 31, 34.
Robertson, George (Artist), 162.
Rodgers, Thomas (Gilder), 17.
Rossi, John Charles Felix (Modeller),
    21, 75, 88.
Royal Family, 85;
    George III, 85.
    Queen Charlotte, 85.
    Royal Children, 85.
Ryland and Coustos, 14.

St Philip, 42.
St Thomas, 42.
Saly, J. F. J., 96.
Sayer and Bennet, 14, 96.
Scheemakers, 76.
Sèvres, 21, 22, 50, 85, 90, 117.
    Figures, 10, 85.
    Seaux à bouteilles, 50, 61.
    Shapes, 10.
Shakespeare, 76, 88, 94.
Shipley, Joseph, 14.
Sims (Gilder), 17.
Smith, Constantine (Painter), 13, 49.
—, Hannah (Née Storer), 49.
—, William (Painter), 13, 18.
—, William (Son of Hannah), 13.
Soar, Thomas (Gilder), 110, 134.
Southall, Thomas (Painter), 13.
Spängler, Jean Jacques, 16, 18, 19,
    21, 88.
Spicers, 20.
Spooner, Jacob, 14, 24.
Spring as a Cherub Candlestick, 65.
Squirrel, 31, *38*.
Stables, Joseph, 11, 17, 19.
Stag and Doe at Lodge, 31, *39*.
Staples, Joseph (Gilder), 135, 146.
Stephan, Pierre, (Artist), 14,
    86, 106.
Stevens, Martin, 17.
Strong, Benjamin, 28.
—, Thomas, 49.
Susini, Giovanni Francesco, 31.

Taylor, 173.
Trundle, Thomas, 14.

Voltaire, 88.
Vien. J. M., 96, 107.
Virtues, The, 87.
Vivares, François, 96.
Vulliamy, 7, 24, 75, 88.

Wardle, Thomas, 14, 153.
Weaver, Samuel, 14.
Webber, Henry (Artist), 74, 75.
Webster (Gilder), 17.
Wedgwood, Josiah, 7, 20, 21, 22, 24,
    29, 74, 75, 86, 88, 95, 96.
Whitehall, William, 14, 27.
Winrow, John (Painter), 13.

Williams, Mr., 15, 24, 74.
Withers, Edward, 19, 116, 143.
Wood, William, 9, 14, 15, 16.
Woodward, Robert, 14, 28.
Worcester Porcelain, 7, 15, 16, 21,
    40, 41, 114, 172.

Yates, John, 105, 139, 161.
— William, 14, 17, 129.

Zoffany, 85.

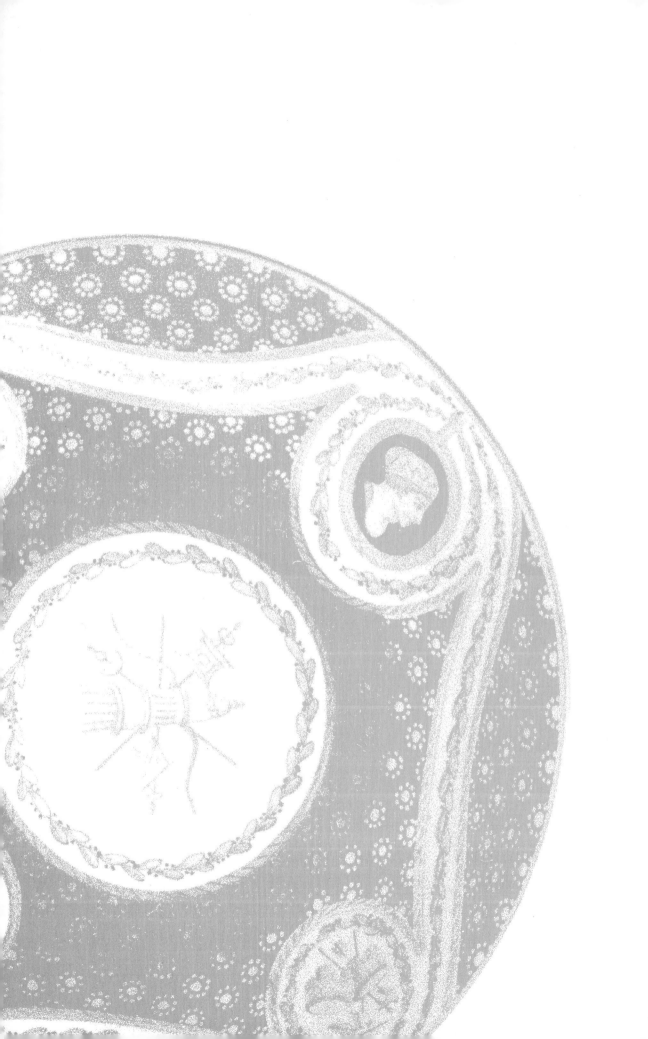